WALK THRU THE

MW00611711

Leading
AND
Loving

DR. BRUCE WILKINSON

**WALK
THRU** THE
BIBLE
CLASSIC

For more than three decades, Walk Thru the Bible has created discipleship materials and cultivated leadership networks that together are reaching millions of people globally through live events, print publications, audiovisual curricula, radio, television, and the Internet. Known for innovative methods and high-quality resources, we serve the whole body of Christ across denominational, cultural, and national lines. Through our strong and cooperative international partnerships, we are strategically positioned to address the church's greatest need: developing mature, committed, and spiritually reproducing believers.

Walk Thru the Bible communicates the truths of God's Word in a way that makes the Bible readily accessible to anyone. We are committed to developing user-friendly resources that are Bible-centered, of excellent quality, lifechanging for individuals, and catalytic for churches, ministries, and movements; and we are committed to maintaining our global reach through strategic partnerships while adhering to the highest levels of integrity in all we do.

Walk Thru the Bible partners with the local church worldwide to fulfill its mission, helping people "walk thru" the Bible with greater clarity and understanding. Live events and small group curricula are taught in over 50 languages by more than 60,000 people in nearly 60 countries, and more than 100 million devotionals have been packaged into daily magazines, books, and other publications that reach over five million people each year. And, in addition to our ever-expanding stock of newly created curricula, we have recently updated Walk Thru the Bible "classics" from every era of our history into digital formats. These resources, new and old, continue to bear fruit in churches, ministries, and individual lives throughout the world.

Walk Thru the Bible

Leading and Loving is designed not simply as a video course, but as a life-changing process. In the next six weeks, you will make a journey that will take you miles down the road toward being an effective leader of your household. Each one of the six video lessons is accompanied by a week's worth of devotional readings, prayers and Scriptures. And there's a lot of searching and growing to be done between lessons. So whether you start the process alone or as part of a group, we strongly encourage you to view just one of the video sessions per week — and let the course take its course in you.

I. VIDEO COURSE NOTES

In each session section, you'll find fill-in-the-blank questions that follow along with the video point by point. As you watch the video, write down key points and Scriptures. This is a vital part of the learning process, a way to make sure that you retain what you learn.

2. VIDEO DISCUSSION QUESTIONS

Throughout each video session, you will see a thought-provoking Discussion Question. Pause the tape at this point and plan to spend about 5-10 minutes on these questions as they appear. This will help each person in your group begin to own the principles presented.

3. SMALL GROUP DISCUSSION QUESTIONS

Following the video course notes for each session, you will find a set of compelling questions to use for group discussion. As you discuss your answers together in the group, you will deepen the process of transformation as you affirm and encourage each other.

4. DAILY DEVOTIONALS

The daily devotionals will challenge you to apply what you've learned to your life. Each devotional provides an introduction, a section of Bible teaching and an application — a summary of practical steps you can take to become a better leader.

5. BIBLE STUDIES

Accompanying sessions 3 and 6, you'll find Bible Studies designed to cement the material you're learning during the week. Use these studies to apply the principles of headship and loving to your life. You may also choose to complete the studies with your wife.

The Role Of The Husband

HEAD

INTRODUCTION

A story of three generations:

_____

_____

Raised by father -

_____

_____

Raised by mother -

_____

_____

Watched by childcare -

_____

_____

BIBLICAL PASSAGES ON MARRIAGE

"For the husband is the head of the wife, as also Christ is head of the church; and He is the Savior of the body…Husbands, love your wives, just as Christ also loved the church and gave Himself for her." Ephesians 5:23, 25-27

"But I want you know that the head of every man is Christ, the head of woman is man, and head of Christ is God. For man is not from woman, but woman from man. Nor was man created for the woman, but woman for the man." I Corinthians 11:3, 8-9

THE HEAD: GOD'S UNIQUE MODEL FOR LEADERSHIP

God is the head of Jesus.

_____

_____

Jesus is the head of man.

_____

_____

Man is the head of wife.

_____

_____

DISCUSSION
When you first got married, what did you think it meant to be the head of your family?

BIBLICAL PERSPECTIVES ON THE MEANING OF "HEAD"

1. You are assigned the_____. *(I Corinthians 11:3; Colossians 1:18)*

2. You are delegated the _____. *(Colossians 2:10; Ephesians 1:22-23)*

3. You bear the_____. *(Colossians 2:19; Ephesians 4:15-16)*

BIBLICAL PORTRAIT OF HEADSHIP
"By God's design, the husband is the head of the wife and lovingly exercises his delegated authority."

BIBLICAL PRINCIPLES FOR THE HEAD

1. The Head of the wife is the husband because of God's _____. *(Ephesians 5:23-24)*

   A. Roles can be defined by our _____.

   B. Roles can be defined by other _____.

   C. Roles can be defined by our _____.

   D. Roles should be defined by God's _____.

DISCUSSION
Why do you think God made man to be the head?

CONCLUSION
Have you ever come before God and accepted your role as the head? No matter where you've been in your marriage, now is the time for you to be the head.

> *"As the head the husband bears the primary responsibility to lead their partnership in a God-glorifying direction. Under God, a wife may not compete for that primary responsibility. It is her husband's just because he is the husband, by the wise decree of God. The ideal of 'equal rights' in an unqualified sense is not Biblical."*
>
> — RAYMOND C. ORTLUND

H E A D

1. Have you ever tried to be the "head" of your wife? If so, what kind of response did you get?

_____

_____

_____

2. How would the average man-on-the-street respond to the statement: "The man is head of the wife"?

_____

_____

_____

3. How would you describe yourself as the "head" of your wife?

How would your wife describe you?

_____

_____

_____

4. What is the biggest frustration you feel about fulfilling your position as "head"?

_____

_____

_____

5. Name one specific situation that you hope will change as a result of this series.

_____

_____

_____

Hebrews 13:7,17 —

> *"Obey those who rule over you...*
> *for they watch out for your souls, as those who must give*
> *account. Let them do so with joy and not with grief, for*
> *that would be unprofitable for you."*

Bob knew that when his 70-year-old dad offered to come over and work on a "project" that there was more at stake than just repairs. Bob, Jr.'s, pickup was about to become the senior Bob's podium.

"Son, you know I try to keep my distance when it comes to your family. I know it's not my place to interfere," began Bob, Sr.

"But..." his son grinned.

"I guess you know me pretty well, huh? Okay, I'll just say it. When your mother and I were over for dinner the other night, I noticed some videos by the VCR that I was a bit surprised to see in your house. I know you don't watch that many movies, so I assume they were Susan's or the kids'. Well, some of them looked pretty marginal — you know, maybe some questionable content.

"I guess I wondered if you knew what movies were in that stack. Are you keeping up with what your family is watching these days? Is it good stuff, consistent with their spiritual development and all?

"Here's my point, Bob. At the church elders' meeting recently, we looked at a verse — Hebrews 13:17 — about church leaders. It says they have to actively watch out for the souls of those they lead because they'll have to give an account to the Lord one day for their leadership and oversight. It made me realize that it's true for the leader of any organization; especially for a husband who has to watch out for his wife and kids. Is this making sense, or am I overstepping my bounds?"

FROM THE WORD

What do you think? Does leadership extend to watching out for the moral and spiritual safety of those you lead?

According to Scripture, the answer is a definite "YES!" The elders referred to in Hebrews 13:7 and 17 were prepared to answer to God for the spiritual growth of those they led. God places leaders over others, including husbands, not only for the direction of their activities but for the care of their souls as well. There is a fine line here, of course. Genuine spiritual leadership does not mean heavy-handed control or undue invasion of privacy. Biblical leaders should demonstrate the same kind of balanced concern that God does.

FOR THE HEART

This is a sensitive area. You may want to discuss it with your wife. But remember, a wife who has been uncared for can feel unloved and insecure. A husband who has crossed the line from concern to control can find his wife resentful of his leadership efforts.

Pick a number between 1 and 10 (1 = ineffective, 10 = very effective) that represents your perception of the your spiritual oversight of your wife. Is it gentle and loving, but clearly evident? Ask your wife the same question, then compare your numbers. Identify your differences, and talk about them together. Side by side, work together to close the gap — at a 10+!

A husband's "soul" job is not his sole job, but close to it!

Ephesians 5:23a —

"For the husband is head of the wife, as also Christ is head of the church."

Betty's tears made silent paths down her cheeks late on a dark winter afternoon. Her quiet sobs and far-off gaze were interrupted as her husband, Gerald, burst through the door, home from another week-long business trip.

"Honey! Here I am! And here's all that's left of my week!" he crowed, hoisting a bag full of dirty clothes bag high like a hunter-gatherer would a downed goose. "Whoa, sweetheart, what's the matter?" offered Gerald, catching sight of Betty's puffy eyes and glistening cheeks.

"It's okay. I'll explain later. Right now, I'm just glad you're home!" said Betty as she gave him a hug.

Over supper, Betty unraveled the feelings that brought the tears: "I came home from work and tried one more time to answer this property tax notice that came Monday. I still couldn't get to the bottom of it, and got all frustrated. I couldn't help thinking about how you used to take care of these things. I wanted to take over the household details now that you're traveling so much, but sometimes I feel like I can't do anything right. It just made me cry."

Gerald struggled silently. He wanted to offer encouragement, but he couldn't think of anything new to say. This was the latest in a long line of details that had gone unresolved since he started the new position with its grueling travel schedule. And Betty was really starting to feel like a failure.

"Honey, let me see if I can make some sense of it," Gerald said. Betty felt relieved. But at the same time, she felt as though she had let Gerald down one more time. No matter how much she tried, she just couldn't seem to fill his shoes when he was away.

FROM THE WORD

Life is not always as tidy as we would like, and Scripture does not directly answer every question. But where the Bible is lacking in specifics, a guiding principle can always be found. In this case, the clear teaching of Ephesians 5:23 is that the man is the head of the wife and of their relationship. He is, therefore, head of their home. Should he be passive, absent, or even verbally abusive, the wife is not promoted to "head of the home," though she may have to perform some of those tasks. While Betty may have to assume some of her husband's duties, she can never totally fill the spot that was meant for him.

FOR THE HEART

What is the status of your marriage? Does your wife feel like you are present or absent? Are you fulfilling your Biblical mandate to be the head of the wife and of your home? Has your wife ever been left to assume the role of head of the marriage or home? Can you name one or two specific things you could do to let your wife know more certainly that you take full responsibility for your household? Write them down right now. Then put them into action today.

Sometimes the best man for the job is the man!

Ephesians 5:23 —

> ## "For the husband is head of the wife, as also Christ is head of the church; and He is the Savior of the body."

The light turned green and David made a left onto the long, straight highway known unofficially as Hamburger Row. "So what are you in the mood for tonight, Jenny?" he asked.

"Oh, I don't know," she said. Jenny seemed far away. This conversation had been going on for the past 20 minutes. And it was the same conversation they always seemed to have around meal time.

"Do you feel like Italian, Chinese, Greek? Hey, we haven't been to the pizza place in a long time."

Suddenly, out of nowhere, Jenny exploded: "I don't care! Why don't you just make a decision of your own?"

David was speechless. He wondered what he had done to deserve an outburst like that. "I'm sorry, I'm sorry," said Jenny, quickly getting a hold of herself. "That was probably uncalled for…it's just that…well, why do I always have to be the one to make the decisions?"

"What do you mean, you *always* make the decisions?" he asked, bewildered.

Jenny seemed flustered, "Oh, I don't know…look, I don't know what's wrong with me. I'm sorry. Let's just forget it."

There wasn't much conversation at dinner. David had plenty of time to think through the situation. It was true that Jenny made a lot of decisions throughout the day. She was the one who checked expenses against the budget. She was the one who did the shopping. She was also in charge of dealing with the health insurance company for reimbursements, and getting the van in for service, and getting the kids to school and to soccer practice. But after all, she was basically the home manager. David was at the office during most daylight hours. He was the breadwinner.

So what was Jenny's problem? Maybe she just needed to count her blessings a little more. Maybe she just needed an attitude check. Right?

HEAD

FROM THE WORD

Maybe not. Ephesians 5:23 states very clearly that the husband is head of the wife. A detailed study of this passage suggests a picture of the man standing physically in front of the wife, perhaps to shield her from potential danger or to represent her in the presence of others.

The idea is that wherever the wife goes, the husband "goes before her." He always sets the direction, and she contributes along the way. She always feels protected. She always feels represented. She never feels alone or overwhelmed. She can always lean on the decision-making skills of her husband. And within the context of that safety, she feels free to operate.

FOR THE HEART

There's a fine line between giving your wife "freedom" and allowing her to become overwhelmed with responsibilities. As the head, it's your job to be sensitive to that issue.

Wives often get a great sense of security from knowing that their man is in charge. That doesn't mean a wife cannot handle a great deal of responsibility. But, the minute she senses she is "going before" her family, the experience begins to turn stressful for her.

How about your wife? Does she feel safe? Or does she sometimes feel like she's "out in front"? Don't be passive in your decision-making. Be bold and decisive, and assure your wife that you set the direction in your marriage.

Keep your marriage going head-first.

1 Corinthians 9:16 —

> *"For if I preach the gospel, I have nothing to boast of,*
> *for necessity is laid upon me;*
> *yes, woe is me if I do not preach the gospel!"*

Near noon on a typical Saturday, Susan was growing a bit frustrated with the answers she was getting from Bob. Her requests had been turned down twice already that morning.

Bob's schedule had been sort of...no, very unreasonable lately, Susan was thinking. It showed on her face, and was about to show in her voice.

"Why are you so busy?" Susan burst out. "Since when does working on our finances and budget take priority over me?"

"What? What's that mean?" Bob asked, pushing back from his desk.

"Well, for the last several weekends, it seems like you've been glued to this desk. Every time I've needed something, you say you don't have time!"

"Well, you know, I guess you're right, Susan. Maybe I haven't explained myself very well. To he honest, I've been a little embarrassed to..."

"Embarrassed about what?" Susan asked, with a little less of an edge.

"Well, ever since Pastor Brennan preached about Paul's life not long ago, on the mandate he had from God, to spread the Gospel? Remember?"

"I remember."

"It was like Paul actually feared not fulfilling the leadership role God had given him. You know, 'Woe is me' if I don't do this. Well, I got to thinking about my leading our family. How I've been putting off doing a budget, and getting our finances in shape. And I started thinking, 'Woe is me!' I guess my need to lead went up a few notches after that sermon!"

FROM THE WORD

Amazing, isn't it? The Apostle Paul was so utterly convinced of his mandate from God — his "need to lead" among the churches — that he feared (in a healthy sense) not doing so! His fear of God drove him daily to fulfill what God had appointed him to do. Granted, Paul was an apostle and we are not. But we are people in various leadership positions in life, all of which we should view like Paul viewed his: I am here by God's appointment. Therefore, I need to fulfill His expectations. I need to lead in this area!

This should especially be true for a husband as he leads his wife.

God's expectations for husbands are as clear as they were for apostles. And since they are God's expectations, our task is clear!

FOR THE HEART

Think about how you are fulfilling the leadership role in your marriage. Do you have a healthy sense of fear, that the Bible presents as a sort of "awesome respect," for God's placement of you as leader in your marriage?

What is the area in which your wife has experienced insecurity or fear due to less-than-ideal leadership? Can you purpose to bless her anew today by leading in a practical way in that area?

Don't let "slow is me" become "woe is me" in your future!

Nehemiah 1:4 —

> ## "So it was, when I heard these words,
> ## that I sat down and wept, and mourned for many days;
> ## I was fasting and praying before the God of heaven."

Justin bounded down the stairs and headed for the front door. "Hold on, son, don't go anywhere right now," Steve called from the study, "We need to have a family meeting this morning."

"Dad, are you kidding? I've got practice in 20 minutes!" pleaded Justin.

Hearing the conflict starting, Karen quickly made her way from the kitchen and intervened. "Honey, Justin's right. Besides, this is not a good time for a family meeting. The estate sale starts at 10 o'clock, and everything will be picked over by noon."

"Well that's one of the things I wanted to talk about," Steve continued, "I'm afraid these weekend estate sales are nickel-and-diming us to death."

Karen stared out the window silently. There was an uncomfortable pause. Steve tried to sound firm as he explained, "I've been thinking about a few things for our family and we just need to talk."

"This is great," Karen thought to herself, "Mr. Control always shows up at the worst times."

Steve went on: "I've been thinking about a lot of things: how to have some quality family time, and how to plan our spending a little better."

"Like how you're planning on spending $50 on golf this afternoon?" Karen quipped.

"Fine!" Steve snarled. "Just go ahead and do whatever you feel like doing. If you don't want to be a family, then I'm not going to force anybody!"

Steve disappeared back into the study and slammed the door. He felt angry, misunderstood, unappreciated. *I try to do something good for my family and that's the kind of thanks I get?* he thought to himself. *See if I try to lead them.*

Steve plopped down in his recliner, turned on the ballgame, and began to quietly nurse his resentment. He was only trying to apply what he had learned at the men's Bible retreat. But it looked like no matter how much he wanted to pull his family together he couldn't force them to cooperate.

FROM THE WORD

Nehemiah was one of the greatest leaders in the Bible. Against tremendous odds and repeated opposition, he rallied the people of Israel to rebuild the city wall in Jerusalem. Painstakingly, he organized every single detail of the operation. He oversaw the financing, he managed the workers, and he devised battle plans to protect against enemy attack. And yet before he did any of this, Nehemiah spent many days fasting and praying in humility before God.

Spiritual leadership not only requires great preparation, but it also requires meaningful interaction with God. Leading a family is not just a physical or social undertaking. It is a spiritual one.

So before you set out to lead your family, you should consult the Lord for some wisdom.

FOR THE HEART

Are you ready to make some changes in the way you lead your family?

Maybe you're looking to fine-tune some areas. Or you could be stepping forward as the head for the very first time. Either way, it can be a touchy subject. There could be many factors that have been at work in your family for a long time. There may be old patterns, old ways of thinking, and maybe even some old wounds.

Have you begun to ask God to show you how to walk step-by-step toward His design for your family? Don't go it alone. God not only designed the original master plan, but he can also help you custom-design a remodeling plan. Humble yourself before Him in prayer. Ask Him to open your eyes to details you may be missing.

If He can show Nehemiah how to restore the city of Jerusalem, then your family should be no problem for Him.

A truly great leader knows Whom to follow.

HEAD

INTRODUCTION

What does it mean to be the head? _____

_____

_____

BIBLICAL PRINCIPLES FOR THE HEAD: (continued)

2. The head is to be the active leader who lovingly _____ and _____.

   A. Rule means _____ and care for the family. *(I Timothy 3:2, 4-5)*

DISCUSSION

What do you do to make your children respect or disrespect you?

   B. Provide means_____ to meet the family's needs. *(I Timothy 5:8)*

BIBLICAL PASSAGES ON HEADSHIP

"A bishop then must be blameless, the husband of one wife, temperate, sober minded, of good behavior, hospitable, able to teach, one who rules his own house well, having his children in submission with all reverence (for if a man does not know how to rule his own house, how will he take care of the church of God?)" I Timothy 3:2, 4-5

"So he went to him and bandaged his wounds, pouring on the oil and wine; and he sent him on his own animal, brought him to an inn, and took care of him. On the next day, when he departed, he took out two denarii, gave them to the innkeeper, and said to him, 'Take care of him; and what ever more you spend, when I come again, I will repay you.'" Luke 10:34-35

"But if anyone does not provide for his own, and especially for those of his household, he has denied the faith and is worse than an unbeliever." I Timothy 5:8

DISCUSSION

What would your wife say you would have to change to become the perfect head?

To "rule" your household means to take care of any need experienced by your wife or children.

THE "HEADSHIP CONTINUUM"

Abandon

Absent

Apathetic

Authentic

Authoritarian

Autocratic

Abusive

3. The Head leads not by "lording it over" or "exercising authority" over his wife, but "with understanding" and by "giving _____."

A. Lording it over abuses personal _____. *(Mark 10:42)*

B. Exercising authority abuses personal _____. *(Mark 10:42)*

BIBLICAL PASSAGE ON HEADSHIP

"Then Jesus called them to himself and said to them, 'You know that those who are considered rulers over the Gentiles lord it over them, and their great ones exercise authority over them. Yet it shall not be so among you; but whoever desires to become great among you shall be your servant.'" Mark 10:42-43

CONCLUSION

Where are you on the "Headship Continuum"? Circle where you are today.

HEAD

1. Has there ever been a time when you "stood before" your wife or children in a real crisis? If so, how do you think it made them feel?

_____

_____

_____

2. How do you think the average man would define the phrase "to rule"?

_____

_____

_____

3. Based on your upbringing, where would you rank your father on the "Headship Continuum"? How has that affected your leadership style with your wife?

_____

_____

_____

4. Can you recall a time when your mother felt a sense of lack of trust in your father? Explain.

_____

_____

_____

5. Where would your wife rank you on the "Headship Continuum"? If you aren't where you should be, what's one change you could make?

_____

_____

_____

1 Samuel 17:37 —

> *"Moreover David said, 'The LORD, who delivered me from the paw of the lion and from the paw of the bear, He will deliver me from the hand of this Philistine.'"*

"Hey, Kathryn! Come on in," Ellen said exuberantly. "Lunch is almost ready."

Kathryn kicked off her sandals beside the door. She hadn't seen her sister Ellen for nearly two weeks. And her sisterly instinct told her that something had changed since they were together last. "Where did you get all these coupons?" Kathryn probed.

"Oh, I've started collecting those to offset some of our grocery expenses."

"Is this another one of Tim's thrifty-nickel budget ideas?" Kathryn said, rolling her eyes.

"You'd be amazed how fast it all adds up," Ellen assured her.

"I'll start collecting coupons when I get to keep the difference in cash," Kathryn scoffed. Now she was visibly upset. She couldn't help comparing her own marriage to her older sister's, and just the mention of finances seemed to hit a sore spot inside. "I can't handle the thought of doing all that work to save a few dollars just so Scott can go out and blow it all at the sporting goods store."

When Scott's name came up, Ellen felt a little uncomfortable. She didn't want to get into another long conversation about his personality flaws right now. "Well, Tim thought it would be a good idea, and I'm willing to try," she added. "It's actually kind of fun."

Kathryn pressed her, "Have you ever figured out how much work you have to do to save one dollar that way? Tim could spend that in one second."

"Look, if you want to know the truth, I'm not really sure it's worth all the effort myself. But Tim was really excited about it, and his instincts usually turn out to be pretty good."

Kathryn just looked away. She realized she didn't have the same kind of trust for her husband that Ellen did. And she wondered how two sisters who started out so similar could have ended up so different.

HEAD

FROM THE WORD

You don't have to know much about the Bible to know the story of David and Goliath. David was just a young man when he faced up to this giant and won. His courage made him a legend. But many people don't realize that David wasn't simply born with giant-slaying courage; he had to develop it over time.

A closer look at the story reveals that Goliath was the latest in a long line of victims in David's wake. While working as a shepherd, David had also killed lions and bears. And through those experiences, David had fine-tuned his faith in God. When it was time to face Goliath, he naturally trusted God.

David's decisions were influenced by God because David was impressed by God's faithfulness. David trusted God with his heart, and with his life! Can you imagine if your wife trusted you like that?

FOR THE HEART

The more we learn about God, the more we realize we can trust Him. The same is true in a marriage relationship. Your wife may sincerely choose to follow you, but unless you have a track record of faithfulness it may be difficult for her to put her heart into it. She may be able to follow you mechanically. But the ultimate goal for the husband is for his wife to experience joy from being under his leadership. That can take time. Especially if she has felt let down in the past.

How about your wife? Is she following you out of duty, or out of joy? If you're honest, you may discover you have some work to do to strengthen your track record of faithfulness. Maybe you could share with her your desire to improve. The more your wife observes your faithfulness through the years, the more she will follow you with heartfelt trust.

"Head" is a position appointed by God. Influence, however, is a privilege earned by man.

When it's easy to trust, it's easy to follow.

John 13:15 —

> ## "For I have given you an example, that you should do as I have done to you."

Bob was concerned, maybe more like frustrated, moving toward angry. Sitting in Pastor Brennan's office, he struggled for the right words to describe his feelings.

"I don't know what's wrong, Jim. No matter what I say to Susan, it seems like I can't get through to her on this. I've tried all the approaches I know. I've said it gently, firmly, creatively, humorously. You name it. I don't know if she's choosing not to respond, or just doesn't care about people!"

"Bob, maybe the problem is not the words you're using, but your own actions. Let me ask you: when was the last time you reached out to a non-Christian neighbor yourself to welcome them to the neighborhood, or help them on a Saturday?"

"Me? Oh, I guess I can't remember. But that's really Susan's job. I mean, she's home all day, and could be having a real impact for Christ on our neighbors. I've asked her to make this a priority, but...well, I've already told you her response."

"Bob, I know Susan, and I know she's not an uncaring neighbor or a rebellious wife. I think she's struggling with your example!"

"You know from your own management experience that people resent being asked to do things that their leaders aren't willing to do, right? Makes them feel used. Here's my idea: No more talk! Instead, why don't you start reaching out to your neighbors. Let's see if your example has a greater impact on Susan than your words have. It couldn't have any less, could it?"

FROM THE WORD

Jesus Christ was not the first person to use an example as a teaching method. His example of washing the disciples' feet, though, is probably the most famous in the world! Could Christ have delivered a lecture, or even told a parable about service, its cost, the humility it requires, its effect on the one served? Of course, and He did speak words to that effect in the Upper Room, but only after He had served them by washing their feet!

His words took on a whole new meaning to the disciples after they saw Him demonstrate how to serve. This is another example of what made Christ the world's greatest leader.

FOR THE HEART

Is there a "sore spot" between you and your wife that is not going away? Something you have asked her to do that she seems resistant or hesitant towards?

While a failure to lead by example is certainly not the cause in every case, it is definitely worth a second look! Stop and think of any areas of your marriage in which your expectations for your wife are higher than your own personal practice. If asking forgiveness is in order, to God or your wife, do so today.

Then, no more talk! Live out what you expect others to do!

Pictures are worth 1,000 words, but actions are worth 1,000,000!

Proverbs 31:10-31 —

> ## "Her husband is known in the gates, when he sits among the elders of the land. Her husband also...praises her."

"Mom!" Lillith exclaimed. "Look at your calendar! You are planning on slowing down one of these years, aren't you?"

Elaine laughed with her daughter. "Maybe someday, dear. But you know your father and I never really believed much in retirement."

"Well, I certainly know what pod this pea came out of," Lillith said confidently, pointing to herself. "You and I are alike in a lot of ways, Mom. Busy, getting things done, making it happen, right? The world needs more women like us, don't you think? Mom? Oh boy, what did I say?"

Sunny, cheerful Elaine became the mom Lillith had seen frequently since her divorce from Larry: sober, concerned, burdened. Whatever she had said, Lillith was sorry it slipped out.

"Lillith, I don't disagree entirely. You and I are somewhat alike. But there is a big difference between what drives you and what drives me. I guess I could illustrate it best by saying that the world doesn't need more women like you and me as much as it needs more men like your father."

"What? Hello-o-o. It's not the Dark Ages, Mom. Remember?"

"I remember all too well," said Elaine. "Lillith, here, take this Bible. Let me show you something."

"Oh, Mom, please, not now." groaned Lillith.

"I think it will help you. When I get back from Vera's in a minute, I'll show you what I'm talking about. It's in Proverbs 31."

FROM THE WORD

Interestingly, Proverbs 31, most noted for its comments about the wife, also offers insight into the role of the husband.

In verses 23 and 28, the husband is pictured as engaged in the civic and professional duties of his day. His leadership style allowed for the full expression of his wife's many and varied talents. He was apparently not threatened by her successes. Rather, he encouraged her to fulfill her role as a wife, which she apparently did exceptionally well! In fact, the text seems to imply that his being "known in the gates" was in no small part due to his wife. His leadership style was mutually beneficial!

FOR THE HEART

How about the husband's leadership style in your marriage?
Is it a style that encourages the wife to be all she can be within her God-given role? Husbands, ask yourself whether any resistance to your leadership from your wife could be stifling her God-given talents. Is your wife content where God has placed her in your marriage?

Identify one way you can more clearly define your role today that at the same time encourages your wife in hers.

Leadership that liberates. Now that's a leadership style!

Revelation 2:4 —

"Nevertheless I have this against you, that you have left your first love."

Ben came running out of the garage holding a bag of golf clubs in his hand. He found his friend, Andy, setting up a card table for the yard sale.

"You're not selling these, are you?" Ben cried in disbelief. He could understand parting with some of the old power tools, but these were Andy's custom-fitted graphite clubs. Everybody knew how much Andy loved them.

"Yeah, I figured I'd let someone else abuse them for awhile," Andy said, with a crooked smile.

"But you just got these last fall and I remember how much you paid for them," said Ben, perplexed. "Is there something wrong with them?"

Finally, Andy faced Ben and prepared to give him a straight answer. "This may sound funny," Andy began, "but I sat down a few weeks ago and figured out how much time I spend on the golf course every year. Care to take a guess?"

"How should I know?" Ben said, "What's the point?"

"320 hours," Andy announced. "That's the same amount of time the average person spends at work over a two month period."

Ben raised his eyebrows, "Wow, two months? That really does add up!"

Andy went on, "Look, I love golf. But do you remember that Bible study we did about loving your wife?" Ben nodded. "I finally realized that it would be a whole lot easier to make Sandra feel loved if I didn't have so many other things to love too. So I'm going to try marriage without golf for a while."

FROM THE WORD

The stern reproof for the Ephesians in Revelation 2:4 serves as a reminder of how easy it is to drift off course. In the same section of Scripture, the Ephesians were commended for their hard work and perseverance. However, they had lost the intensity of their first love. And this was a source of grief to God. Perhaps there were other interests that popped up gradually over time. At first they didn't appear to hinder the Ephesians' primary purpose. But eventually, they managed to dilute the passion that they once had.

It's easy to get much too busy in this day and age. And while we might love nothing more than our wife and family, other interests can keep us from loving them like we should.

FOR THE HEART

You have been called to love your wife the way Christ loves the church. That's a tall order. Can you think of anything that competes for your first love? It may be a hobby, a pastime, or even work. Of course, this doesn't mean you shouldn't work, or have hobbies. But maybe it's time to simplify your life a little to allow more of your love to go where it was intended. There's a great sense of fulfillment that comes when everything you do supports your first calling to be the head of your family.

Don't spread yourself, or your love, too thin.

Ephesians 5:28-29 —

> ### "So husbands ought to love their own wives
> ### as their own bodies; he who loves his wife loves himself.
> ### For no one ever hated his own flesh, but nourishes and
> ### cherishes it, just as the Lord does the church."

"I'll be right there, Becky," John called from the bedroom, "just let me find my cuff links."

It was the night of the Management Appreciation Dinner, and for Becky it was her first chance to spend an evening with her husband since their anniversary. John rummaged through the top drawer of the dresser trying to remember where he had left his cuff links.

He pushed a pile of socks out of the way and uncovered a stack of photographs. There, on the top, was a picture of a woman he almost didn't recognize. It was Becky. He picked up the picture and was instantly thrown back in time. He could recall the moment like it was yesterday.

They were on a weekend to trip to the mountains. It was eight years ago. She was standing on the deck on the back of the cabin. It was supposed to be a picture of the view through the trees, but Becky turned around right as the camera snapped and her natural smile was captured in a way no posed picture ever could. She looked so happy and excited then. What had happened?

Physically, she hadn't changed much in eight years. But it seemed like she was always under stress now. There were more and more things to do. By the time she finished running the kids around and cleaning up the house all day, she could hardly wait to lie down and catch her breath.

As he stared at the photograph, John longed to have the old Becky back. He recalled what Pastor Brennan had been saying about how a woman's eyes say a lot about her husband. It finally sunk in. And right there in his bedroom, John committed himself to try to restore the joy in Becky's life.

FROM THE WORD

Neither Jesus nor the apostle Paul ever married. And yet, from their words we get some of the most vivid, detailed instructions on how to be a successful husband. In Ephesians, Paul paints a picture of the wife as virtually an extension of the man's own body. Then he presents the concept of carefully cultivating and developing the wife, tenderly bringing her to full-bloom. These passages convey the image of a man who is virtually preoccupied with helping his wife reach her potential, both in terms of achievement and in joy.

As head, you are the key to helping your wife be everything God wants her to be. You either help that cause, or hinder it.

FOR THE HEART

Is there something missing in your wife's life right now? Like a meticulous gardener, you are responsible for providing just the right balance of elements to create the optimal environment for her growth. Is there something you could be doing to encourage your wife to help her grow spiritually or to help her blossom the way God intended her to? Why not take a few moments to humbly pray and then take immediate steps to bring that sparkle back into your wife's eyes.

If your wife is living in the Dark Ages, then you could be "the missing link."

HEAD

INTRODUCTION

How do you know how you're doing as the head?

BIBLICAL PRINCIPLES FOR THE HEAD (continued)

3. The Head leads not by "lording it over" or "exercising authority" over his wife, but "with

   understanding" and by "giving _____."

   C. With understanding means to have intimate _____. *(I Peter 3:7)*

   D. Giving honor means to value her through "portions of _____." *(I Peter 3:7)*

BIBLICAL PASSAGES ON HEADSHIP

*"Likewise you husbands, dwell with them with understanding, giving honor to the wife,
as to the weaker vessel, and as being heirs together of the grace of life, that your prayers may not
be hindered." I Peter 3:7*

*"Husbands, love your wives, just as Christ also loved the church and gave Himself for her, that
He might sanctify and cleanse her with the washing of water by the word, that He might present
her to Himself a glorious church, not having spot or wrinkle or any such thing, but that she
should be holy and without blemish." Ephesians 5:25-27*

*"Moreover Christ does not lead the church as his daughter but as his wife. He is preparing her to be a
'fellow-heir,' not a servant girl. Any kind of leadership that in the name of Christlike headship tends
produce in a wife personal immaturity or spiritual weakness or insecurity through excessive control or
picky supervision or oppressive domination has missed the point of the analogy in Ephesians 5. Chris
does not create that kind of wife."*

— JOHN PIPER

4. The Head submits to God's primary call to be his wife's head and devotes himself to her above

   children, friends, recreation, ministry, or _____. *(Ephesians 5:25-29)*

DISCUSSION

What would your wife say is the most important thing in your life?

5. The head is the spiritual leader who nurtures his wife to become blameless, holy, and

_____. *(Ephesians 5:25-27)*

  A. Blameless means without fault in character and _____.

  B. Holy means separated from sin and consecrated to _____.

  C. Glorious means held in high honor and radiantly _____.

DISCUSSION

What two or three things could you do to help your wife blossom as a woman?

PERSONAL PROGRESS IN THE HUSBAND'S ROLE AS HEAD

PROGRESS POINTS	progress needed	progress acceptable	progress great
1. The husband accepts God's call to be head.	☐	☐	☐
2. The husband lovingly rules and provides well.	☐	☐	☐
3. The husband doesn't lord it over his wife but treats her with understanding and honor.	☐	☐	☐
4. The husband is deeply devoted to his wife above all.	☐	☐	☐
5. The husband nurtures his wife to become blameless, holy, and glorious.	☐	☐	☐

1. I think the area in which the husband does best as head is _____.

2. The part of this session that meant the most to me about the husband being the head of the

  wife was _____.

3. One thing the husband could do right now in his role as head that would mean a great deal to

  the wife would be _____.

PRACTICAL POINTERS ON THE ROLE OF HEAD

1. _____ any feelings of inadequacy, fear, and anxiety about your role through Biblical

 solutions.

 A. Inadequacy is overcome through James 1:4-8.

 B. Fear is overcome through 2 Timothy 1:7.

 C. Anxiety is overcome through Philippians 4:6-7.

2. _____ spiritually mature married men to meet with you regularly for support and

 accountability. *(Proverbs 15:22; 11:14; 18:1)*

 A. Who?

 B. When?

 C. Where?

 D. How often?

3. _____ for your own spiritual life and the spiritual lives of your wife and

 family. *(Ephesians 5:25-27)*

 A.   Read the Bible each day.

 B.   Pray for your wife specifically each day.

 C.   Pray for her hopes and dreams.

 D.   Pray for her struggles and challenges.

 E.   Pray for her spiritual life and growth

 F.   Attend church regularly.

 G.   Participate in a small group for spiritual growth and discipleship.

 H.   Serve the Lord daily.

4. _____ regularly that God called you to be the head of your wife — and as you lead,

 "do it heartily, as to the Lord and not to men." *(Colossians 3:23)*

THE ROLE OF THE MAN
IN MARRIAGE:

Protector

Provider

Point man

Problem-solver

Physician

Priest

Prince

PERSONAL PLEDGE

Get alone with your wife and review the following statements together. Discuss them briefly together. Explain your desire to move in the direction of becoming a loving leader. Then speak your personal pledge to her out loud. If she feels comfortable, your wife may join you in the joint pledge and then speak the wife's pledge to you.

TOGETHER: We affirm today that God designed the husband to be the head of the wife. We willingly choose to submit to God's designed for our marriage.

HUSBAND: I commit to you that I will respond to God's call on my life to be your head. I ask for your forgiveness for the times I have failed you and not been the head that the Lord expects me to be. I hereby pledged to be an active leader who serves you with an understanding and gentle Spirit.

WIFE: I commit to you that I will respond to God's call on my life to follow you as my head. I ask for your forgiveness for the times I have struggled against you as my head and therefore not pleased the Lord. I hereby pledge to give you my respect and follow you as my head.

SINGLE: I commit to honor and implement God's decision for the husband to be the head of the wife. I yield myself to His perfect design for the role of the husband in marriage, and purpose today to prepare myself mentally, spiritually, emotionally, and practically to carry out his design in anticipation of my own future marriage.

CONCLUSION

The man is the head of the wife. Christ's love for the church is his model for headship.

H E A D

1. Has there ever been a time when you gave a "portion of preciousness" to your wife? Describe.

_____

_____

_____

2. What are some examples of how you use "intimate perception" to know how your wife is doing?

_____

_____

_____

3. When during your marriage have you seen your wife blossom or wilt? Give examples.

_____

_____

_____

4. Is your wife the most important thing in your life?

What would you say are the top 3 things that compete for that position in day-to-day life?

_____

_____

_____

5. What do you do that really makes your wife feel "gorgeous"? Describe.

_____

_____

_____

Matthew 6:21 —

"For where your treasure is, there your heart will be also."

"So are you coming over to watch the game Saturday?" Steve asked.

"No," Bill explained, "Carol and I are going to do some yard work that afternoon."

"Yard work?" said Steve, in disbelief. "You hate yard work! If you don't mind my asking, what's gotten into you lately? You never do any 'guy' things anymore."

"I don't really hate yard work," Bill replied. It was true that Bill had turned Steve down a lot more lately. And having known him since college, Steve made it his duty to point it out every time Bill showed signs of maturing.

"I don't know if I could ever be like you," Steve reasoned. "I guess you really are more of the family-man type than I am," he added.

"What does that mean?" Bill said.

"I don't know. It just seems like you and Carol just get closer and closer while Julie and I keep drifting farther and farther apart. Don't get me wrong, I'm committed to our marriage. It's just that sometimes it doesn't seem like much of a marriage."

"Can I be totally honest?" Bill asked.

"Go ahead," Steve invited.

"I did hate yard work," Bill explained. "In fact, there wasn't much we both got excited about once those honeymoon years were over. But I just decided I could either do my own thing, or try to find our thing."

"Yeah, but aren't you really just doing her thing?' Steve asked.

"It felt like that at first," said Bill. "But it's funny. Now I'm actually starting to enjoy things that I thought I didn't like. I guess you can choose what you want to like."

FROM THE WORD

In the Sermon on the Mount, Jesus presents a powerful principle. He explains that a man's heart follows his treasure. In other words, whenever a man invests himself in something, it eventually becomes the object of his heart. To the casual observer, it appears to be the other way around. First, we experience the desire to do something, then we do it. But Jesus' statement reveals that over the long term, the very root of our desires is ultimately a matter of choice.

Your desires are constantly changing. You can allow them to wander randomly, feeding themselves in a self-perpetual cycle. Or you can influence them by the deliberate act of your will.

FOR THE HEART

Do you ever struggle with making your wife your first desire? Does it sometimes feel like you would exhaust yourself if you tried to pursue her interests any more? Does it feel like what you really need is a little more time for yourself?

Maybe you should consider this principle. It could be that your desires are pulling you away from your family, instead of toward them. You can begin now to steer the desires of your heart in your wife's direction. It may take discipline and sacrifice. But before long, you will reap the rewards of being "well-invested" in your family.

If your heart is in your marriage, then your heart's in the right place.

Romans 8:9a —

> ## "But you are not in the flesh but in the Spirit...."

It began as a simple exercise, but as Greg listened to the results he could hardly believe his ears.

The men of his Sunday school class were asked to interview their wives on an interesting topic: "In what ways do I act like my father?"

The assignment called for the wives to report on a wide variety of subjects including their husband's attitudes about work, household chores, parenting, romance, and even cooking.

Each husband was to present the questionnaire to his wife and give her 24 hours to complete it. They would discuss their answers on the following Sunday.

Greg's wife Judy was somewhat familiar with Greg, Sr., but since there were over a hundred miles between them, Greg expected her responses to the questionnaire to be somewhat neutral. He was in for a surprise.

Judy not only had strong opinions on almost every topic, but she provided several examples from their marriage in the margins along the side of the page. She included descriptions of his mannerisms and several phrases that Greg commonly repeats in various situations.

Greg was speechless. But as he analyzed each response, he was unable to deny a single one. Those were his views about work. He did believe parenting should work that way. And come to think of it, he does say that whenever another motorist makes him upset.

He had never thought about it. He had certainly never planned for it. And judging by his reaction to the survey, he had never even realized it. Good thing for Greg and Judy that for the most part Greg's father was a godly, conscientious husband.

FROM THE WORD

Perhaps you've seen the bumper sticker that says, "It's official. I have become my mother!" While it strikes a humorous note, it also points to a real tendency. Our perceptions of marriage are strongly influenced by what our parents modeled out in front of us. The way you understand the role of husband is no exception. There's just one problem. Your father may or may not have followed a Biblical model on all points.

It could be that you have been given a great role model in your father. But God's Word tells us we should always look to our Heavenly Father's example first, an example that is described in detail in the Bible.

FOR THE HEART

People can react to their upbringing in a number of different ways. Some mimic the example they saw growing up. Others swing to the opposite extreme, determined not to repeat their parents' mistakes. Neither of these approaches ensures a Biblical perspective.

Does your concept of "husband" bear the influence of your Heavenly Father? Or would you say it mostly reflects your earthly father's? Are there some areas that have yet to be brought through the refining fire of God's Word? Take a few moments to come before God on this issue. What is one trait your father had that you have, but wish you didn't? Why not take this week to consciously unravel this family trait!

Father knows best, but your Heavenly Father knows even better!

1 Timothy 3:5 —

> ### "For if a man does not know how to rule his own house, how will he take care of the church of God?"

The small group Bible study was about to wrap up. Pastor Brennan closed his Bible and invited the men in his office to share their comments. Jeff promptly jumped in, "I can see why Paul said it would be better to remain single. Family duties really have a way of hindering ministry."

Everyone grew a little uncomfortable. They were all friends, but it was no secret that Jeff and Linda were going through a hard time. Jeff was an eager, growing Christian with a strong desire to witness about his faith. Linda was a believer too, but Jeff's zeal was putting a lot of extra demands on their family.

"How so, Jeff?" Pastor Brennan asked. "Well, obviously if I'm spending time taking care of my family, that's time I'm not spending out doing ministry somewhere."

The room erupted with comments as several men identified flaws in Jeff's logic. Pastor Brennan moderated, "Hold on, men. Jeff, go ahead."

"Well, take the Wild Game Dinner we held last week. That was tough to pull together, but eight men indicated they wanted to know more about God. Just think how many of those dinners we could do each year if all of us were single."

Pastor Brennan recalled the afternoon recently when Linda phoned his wife Cindy in tears over the fact that she had 400 brownies to bake for the Wild Game Dinner. Cindy ended up doing most of it so Linda could get the house ready for Jeff's parents to visit that weekend.

Finally, Bill spoke up, "I look at it this way: I may not always be out doing ministry somewhere, but when I'm *really* with my family I'm always doing ministry."

The room was silent. No one meant to put Jeff down. But the truth of Bill's words cut like a knife.

FROM THE WORD

Often, following God is a matter of knowing when to elevate certain Biblical principles over others. To the Corinthians, Paul wrote about the advantages of remaining unmarried. But in his letter to Timothy, Paul speaks very clearly about the ministry responsibilities of a married man. In 1 Timothy 3:5, Paul's words suggest that leadership at home is a type of prerequisite for leadership in the church.

Inevitably, many men skip the first step and start looking for outside ministries to serve. This is even more tempting when there are problems at home. But as Paul explains, when you accept the role of "head," your first priority is to be to personal priest to your family. Often, God uses this environment to prepare men to lead in other capacities.

FOR THE HEART

Do you have a heart to serve God? Are you eager to get out and serve God in a "big" way? Have you ever overlooked the ministry to which God appointed you the title of President — your family?

Have you ever felt frustrated because your duties at home were preventing you from blossoming on the "mission field"? Perhaps it's time to turn and embrace the very things that frustrate you. Make them the object of your ministry. It may even be appropriate to ask forgiveness of your wife or children.

Take a moment to get before God and renew your commitment to serve Him in ministry, starting right at home.

God made you the head of your family, not the head of the world!

Genesis 3:17b —

"Cursed is the ground for your sake; in toil you shall eat of it all the days of your life."

Something was different. When Bob walked in, there were flowers on the table, candles, and a large pot roast — his favorite! "What's this for?" Bob asked.

"I just wanted to thank you for making the Women's Shelter's first Silent Auction such a huge success," Sarah beamed.

"What do you mean?" Bob asked. "That whole thing was your idea."

"Yeah, but it was you who decided to make some tough changes in our family a few years ago," Sarah explained. "I remember how skeptical I was at first."

Two years earlier, Bob had become convinced that they should be setting their budget based on his salary alone. Anything Sarah earned would be "extra." In the process, Sarah eventually decided to quit her job and put her career on hold for a while.

About the same time, Sarah learned of a group of women who were in dire need of shelter, clothing, and a fresh start. Her heart became increasingly burdened with a desire to help them. Before long, Sarah had almost single-handedly established a permanent shelter for women in need.

Sarah went on, "I never imagined how perfectly my job skills had prepared me to help needy women this way."

"You have a lot of talents," Bob added. "That's why your career took off the way it did."

"Looking back, I realize that this is something I've always wanted to do," Sarah pondered. "And if it hadn't been for you, I would have never even known I had this dream."

FROM THE WORD

In Genesis 3:16-19, God sentenced Adam and Eve (and the entire human race) to their respective lots in life. To Eve, He greatly increased the pain of childbirth. To Adam, He caused the act of finding food to become a burden. In that moment, the circumstances of life changed for all of us.

God designed man and woman. And in this passage, He modified the blueprint somewhat. His judgments were very specific, and in them we find the updated plan for how men and women function: The woman labors in childbirth; and the man is to bear his burden in toiling for food. It was not a joint sentencing. The woman was not intended to bear the man's burden any more than the man was intended to feel birth pangs.

FOR THE HEART

Husband, does your wife share the burden of providing for the family? If so, she may be serving a sentence she was never given! God has already decided her portion. Don't add to it. It's one thing if she chooses to work. But if it's out of necessity, because of your poor planning or budgeting, then it's not really the way God re-designed it.

This can be a touchy subject for couples. Financial demands are very real. Lifestyles may be well established. If this concept catches you off guard, don't let it overwhelm you.

If this area is perhaps off-balance in your marriage, why not take your wife out for a special dinner and initiate a heart-to-heart conversation. Ask her this open-ended question, "If you could change this, what would you do?"

He who wears the pants in the family must also carry the wallet.

1 Timothy 5:8 —

> *"But if anyone does not provide for his own,*
> *and especially for those of his household,*
> *he has denied the faith and is worse than an unbeliever."*

Dennis was uncomfortable. But he couldn't quite put his finger on it. The family just seemed a little too out of control for his liking. Austin's latest temper tantrum had resulted in a shoe-sized hole in his bedroom wall. Little Amy seemed to be whining more instead of less. In all, there was just a basic element of respect that was missing from the children.

Out of patience, and out of ideas, Dennis collapsed into his easy chair. It had been a great week at work, but an exhausting one. In fact, it had been a great month and a great year. He was more than meeting all of his quotas. The bonuses were rolling in. And this streak that he had been on for three years showed no signs of ending.

But somehow it seemed the harder he worked, the less progress he saw at home. Sure, they seemed to have plenty of money for all the things they needed. The kids had all the right clothes, the best toys, and they really seemed to like private school.

In just about every category, Dennis had accomplished the goals he had set for himself, including reaching the point where Stephanie would no longer have to work. But now, even she seemed to act a bit distant around him.

It was because of his family that he decided to take on his new position. It would afford them a better quality of life. But now it seemed like Stephanie only talked about how much she wished Dennis could be around more. It seemed no matter how much he gave, it just wasn't enough.

FROM THE WORD ☐

"Providing" for the family can mean different things to different people. To some, it's simply a matter of keeping everyone warm and fed. To others, the package includes braces, college tuition, a first car, and a portfolio of mutual funds. So how do you know where to set your standard?

The Bible doesn't point to a single standard of living set for everyone.

Instead, Scripture suggests a different way of looking at it. In the original Greek, the word "provide" means "to take thought for." This concept goes beyond basic food, water, and shelter. When you sincerely take thought for someone, you will carefully notice when that person has any kind of need, including emotional or spiritual. In essence, "providing" requires being well-attuned to all the needs of the other person, and as sensitive to their needs as you are to your own.

FOR THE HEART

When you think of "providing" for someone, do you only think in terms of material things? Or do you view yourself as taking thought of the whole person? A well-timed hug can be more satisfying than a full-course meal. Material things are important, but they are not a very good measuring stick for a person's level of need. Some of the neediest people are those with a great abundance of possessions.

Don't make the mistake of judging your performance based on things.

A good provider is someone with a sixth sense for the needs of his wife and family. Someone whose radar is constantly scanning, ready to detect when a need arises. Is there any need your wife has right now that you could meet for her?

Shower them with the best presents: your presence!

The fact is, God did. And what an exciting and awesome challenge it is!

Do not allow yourself to be overwhelmed in the task. Do not give in to any fear of failure. And do not get angry or frustrated at God for ordaining the husband as the leader in marriage.

Do ask God for wisdom. Do search the Scriptures for help. And do commit yourself to apply these principles in your own life and marriage, even today.

1. *Leadership by design* Ephesians 5:23

What role is the husband designated to fill in marriage?

List at least three areas in which a husband should lead his wife.

Who would your friends say is usually the leader in your marriage? Why would they say that?

What is the one area in your marriage in which you need to lead your wife more effectively?

2. *A bold leader* Genesis 12:1-5

What instruction did Abraham immediately obey that had a radical impact on Sarah's life?

In what types of difficult and challenging situations does a husband need to lead with boldness?

What bold step of leadership have you taken in your marriage that was tough for you, but right for the family? In what area is it particularly difficult for you to exercise leadership right now in your marriage?

What steps of action do you believe Abraham would advise you to take in the face of this challenge?

3. *A role surrendered* Genesis 16:1-6

In Genesis 13:16, what did God promise Abraham?

In Genesis 16, how did Abraham surrender leadership to Sarah?

Name a couple of situations which tempt you to surrender leadership to your wife.

Have you surrendered leadership to the wife at any time in your marriage? If so, give an example.

How could you avoid this mistake in the future?

4. ***Ruling as a role*** *1 Timothy 3:4-5; 12*

What reputation is a godly husband to have in relation to his family?

What types of behaviors have you observed in men who seem to be good leaders in their marriages?

Identify several ways you fulfill your role as the leader in your marriage.

What needs to be changed for you to be seen more clearly as the leader in your marriage?

5. ***The spiritual leader*** *Job 1:1-5*

How did Job exercise spiritual leadership in his home?

What are at least two things a contemporary husband could do to be a spiritual leader to his wife?

What are the greatest hindrances you face in being the spiritual leader of the home?

In your marriage, what is the most important thing you could do to lead your wife spiritually?

Will you honor God's plan to establish the husband as the leader in your marriage?
Signify your commitment by initialing and dating this page.

_____   _____
YOUR INITIALS   TODAY'S DATE

The
Responsibility
Of The
Husband

INTRODUCTION
Where does love originate in the family?

BIBLICAL PASSAGES ON LOVING YOUR WIFE
"Husbands, love your wives, just as Christ also loved the church and gave Himself for her. So husbands ought to love their own wives as their own bodies; he who loves his wife loves himself. For no one ever hated his own flesh, but nourishes it and cherishes it, just as the Lord does the church. Nevertheless let each one of you in particular so love his own wife as himself, and let the wife see that she respects her husband." Ephesians 5:25, 28-29, 33

"Husbands, love your wives and do not be bitter toward them." Colossians 3:19

"Love suffers long and is kind; love does not envy; love does not parade itself, is not puffed up; does not behave rudely, does not seek its own, is not provoked, thinks no evil; does not rejoice in iniquity; but rejoices in the truth; bears all things, believes all things, hopes all things, endures all things. Love never fails." I Corinthians 13:4-8a

BIBLICAL PERSPECTIVES ON LOVE

1. Perspective #1: Love that is _____. *John 3:16, Matthew 5:44*

2. Perspective #2: Love that is _____. *John 15:13, Romans 5:8, I John 3:18*

DISCUSSION
What secrets have you learned about how to love your wife regardless of how you feel?

3. Perspective #3: Love that is _____. *Matthew 6:24, I John 2:15, Revelation 12:11*

BIBLICAL PORTRAIT OF LOVE
"As head of the wife, the husband chooses to love his wife unconditionally,

sacrificially, and loyally as Christ loved the church."

BIBLICAL PRINCIPLES ON LOVING YOUR WIFE

1. Love your wife because God commands you to _____.

   A. Present tense – I am to love _____.

DISCUSSION
What should you do the next time you're tempted to stop loving your wife?

   B. Active voice – I am to love _____.

> *"True love doesn't have a happy ending; true love doesn't have an ending."*

> *"Love is the one business in which it pays to be absolutely lavish: give it away; throw it away; splash it over; empty your pockets; shake the basket; and tomorrow you'll have more than ever."*

   C. Imperative mood – I am to love by my _____.

> *"We have a picture of the perfect partner, but we marry an imperfect person. Then we have two options. Tear up the picture and accept the person, or tear up the person and accept the picture."*
> – J. GRANT HOWARD, JR.

CONCLUSION
Take your picture of the "perfect person" and set it aside. Then turn to your wife and love her just the way she is.

L O V E

1. When in your marriage are you the most tempted to stop loving your wife?

_____

_____

_____

2. By our culture's standards, when is it okay to stop loving your wife? By God's standards?

_____

_____

_____

3. Describe the last time you struggled to show "unconditional" love to your wife.

_____

_____

_____

_____

4. In your marriage, how do you know when your wife has "received" your love?

_____

_____

_____

5. If you are honest with yourself, can you name something you expect from your wife in return for your love? Can you think of Bible verses that address your expectation?

_____

_____

_____

Ephesians 5:29 —

> ## *"For no one ever hated his own flesh, but nourishes and cherishes it, just as the Lord does the church."*

John kissed his wife Rebecca and dropped his briefcase on the sofa with a thud. It had been another one of those long days.

"I ran into Alice at the store today," Rebecca reported. "She said that Jerry and Ed are going fishing next weekend. I wish you could go with them."

John could hardly believe his ears. She wished he could go fishing? Surely, he had misunderstood her.

Back before the kids were born, John had been an avid fisherman. In fact, his frequent trips had been a big part of their marriage difficulties for a while. But a lot had changed since those days. John was a totally different husband. He worked hard to put Rebecca first, to nourish her, and to make sure she felt cared for. He was almost incapable of imagining a fishing trip with the guys. But did she really just say that she wished he could go?

"Yeah, but we're cleaning out the basement that weekend, remember?" John said, unwilling to get his hopes up.

"Oh, the basement can wait, don't you think?" Rebecca answered. "This sounds like an excellent opportunity for you to get out with the guys."

"Are you being serious?" John's eyes began to beam with new life. He could almost hear the "plunk" of the lure hitting the water. He could smell the fresh earth that contained a twisted mass of red wiggler worms.

John came back to reality again, "What about the kids?"

"Oh I can handle them myself for the weekend," she insisted. "Come on, why don't you give Jerry a call right now?"

"Well, if that's what it takes to make you happy," John said with smirk.

FROM THE WORD

We are surrounded by messages encouraging us to love ourselves more than our spouses. We are told, "watch your back," and "watch out for #1." Ironically, this approach only breeds an environment where it is increasingly necessary to exercise self-defense. But God has a better plan in mind.

LOVE

In Ephesians 5:29, Paul reveals a mystery. He explains that in the light of God's view of marriage being "one flesh," loving your spouse is the only appropriate response. And when we do so, we often end up experiencing more love ourselves.

FOR THE HEART

How about your marriage? Are you only looking out for #1? Or are you equally determined to make sure your wife feels "nourished" and "cherished"? It's easy for couples to get in the pattern of watching out only for themselves. But over time, you can turn things around.

When you don't put others first, you put yourself first. This is at the core of man's spiritual struggle — to deny self and to serve God. Loving your wife is a simple matter of obedience. Right now, list three ways you can make your wife "feel" loved today. Then get to work loving her!

Do unto your wife as you would have her do unto you.
Now that's a golden rule!

1 John 4:19 —

"We love Him because He first loved us."

Jim found the pastor's question intriguing: "What's your L.Q.?" Jim had never thought about his love quotient.

The concept of I.Q. was all too familiar to Jim. He had heard it all his life. Class valedictorian, Phi Beta Kappa, Summa Cum Laude, and now a successful career in business.

Jim seemed to excel naturally in school and in the workplace. It was almost effortless. But for some reason, the home front was a different story. His marriage wasn't in trouble or anything. It's just that for all the work he put into it, the challenge only seemed to get bigger and bigger.

Being an intelligent guy, Jim took his marriage vows to heart. He understood the emphasis on love. Over the years, he had read books and books about relationships and making marriage work. He knew in his heart that love was the whole key. But for the first time in his life, Jim was facing a roadblock he couldn't solve. How does a person generate more love?

Whenever Jim had needed more knowledge, or more information, or more experience, he simply went out and got it. He prided himself in his resourcefulness. But now he was embracing the fact that this issue of love was deeply mysterious. Somehow it was spiritual.

And when the pastor suggested that a person could increase his love quotient dramatically, Jim was all ears.

FROM THE WORD

Have you ever thought about your "love quotient"? Your intelligence quotient pretty much stays the same throughout your life. But your love quotient has the potential to greatly increase. Imagine having a greater capacity to love people, even those it's difficult to love! The apostle John explained the secret of increasing your love quotient. Our love, he explains, is the natural response to the love we receive from the Lord. To the degree that we have experienced love, we will give it.

FOR THE HEART

How about you? Is your love for your wife funded by the Source of unconditional love: God? God has instructed you to love your wife the way Christ loved the church: thoroughly, continuously, and indefinitely. That's not an easy task! If you love using only your own resources, you'll run out too soon.

Has there ever been a time when you received God's love by inviting the Lord Jesus into your heart? If not, then you have no access to the real power of love He intended you to employ. If you're not sure, why not talk to your pastor or a Christian friend who can introduce you to Jesus Christ! If you have already made that decision, are you truly tapping into that love on a daily basis through prayer, Bible study, and meditating on Scripture?

Take a moment to celebrate God's love for you and refresh your commitment to love the way you have been loved.

Hurt people hurt people. Loved people love people.

Hosea 2:19 —

"I will betroth you to Me forever; yes, I will betroth you to Me in righteousness and justice, in lovingkindness and mercy;"

"Dr. Rutledge will be right with you," came the voice over the phone. Drew shifted his weight in his recliner as the on-hold music began to play. He had never talked to a pastor about a personal problem. But now he was convinced that unless he sought qualified advice he could be stuck in this rut for the rest of his married life.

Despite his efforts to have a growing marriage, Drew felt like his life was one, continuous instant-replay. Month after month he seemed to repeat the same cycle. First, he would shower Gail with love; before long, her imperfections would begin to wear on his nerves and his love would become labored; eventually, when he couldn't take any more, he would blow his stack; finally, he would repent and vow to shower her with love again. No matter how sincere his re-commitments, the pattern continued.

"Drew, are you there?" Dr. Rutledge broke in. For the next 20 minutes, Drew described his situation in detail. He told of how he had once regretted marrying someone with such a strong personality. He told of their progress since the days when they used to have terrible arguments. He told of his commitment to be a husband who loves unconditionally. "But why," Drew begged, "can't I seem to break out of this rut? Why do I always end up getting so frustrated?"

Dr. Rutledge listened carefully. Then he posed an unexpected and penetrating question: "Drew, what does God expect from you in return for His love?"

Drew thought carefully. He considered that God probably expects Christians to live morally, to treat each other right, and to spread His love throughout the world. But the more Drew thought about it, he realized that those things might please God, but He really didn't expect them as a condition for His love. Finally, Drew answered, "Nothing, I guess."

Dr. Rutledge went on to suggest that the one of greatest causes of conflict in relationships is our unmet expectations. "Somehow, people have a way of re-writing the plan on God," he explained. "We get it in our heads how things should go, and when they don't, we get frustrated. That's why it's best just to stick to what God says. Don't expect more than what He promises. He says He'll take care of us, and we just have to trust Him to do it."

FROM THE WORD

Undoubtedly one of the most shocking pictures of married life in the Bible is the story of Hosea. Ironically, it also provides one of the best role models for husbands today. The book of Hosea records how he married a harlot named Gomer who sought affairs with other lovers and deserted Hosea. Eventually, Hosea literally bought Gomer back at the slave market and restored her to himself.

Despite great obstacles, Hosea succeeded as a husband. And the key to his success was his level of expectation. Hosea saw himself as a man on a mission. His job was to take a wife, Gomer, and to love her. Beyond that, he had no expectations. His love was not contingent on how Gomer performed.

FOR THE HEART

Husbands are commanded to love their wives. But there's a tendency to build expectations into that command. We think that if we do a good job of loving, we'll eventually get something in return. If you try harder, then she'll try harder, right? Not necessarily. If your goal is to change your wife, or to get her to give you something in return, you could be setting yourself up for disappointment and frustration. You are not commanded to elicit some type of behavior from her, but to love her without any conditions.

Is there something you expect from your wife in return for loving her? Or are you looking to God to meet your needs as you obey His command to love her? When you surrender your expectations, you clear the way for God to change your wife in His timing. After all, that's what it means to love her "for better or for worse."

Don't let great expectations become great frustrations.

Proverbs 21:23 —

> ## "Whoever guards his mouth and tongue keeps his soul from troubles."

Oops! That's the only word that could adequately describe how Marcus felt. He didn't mean to say what he had just said. It just sort of slipped out. And now Dana stared off into her magazine while her face turned red with anger.

"I didn't mean it, honey," Marcus began. "Please, just let me explain."

It was too late. Marcus had said it. In time, neither he nor Dana would even recall the exact words he said. Just that they were cutting, harsh, and bitter. And no matter how much he wished he could take them back, he couldn't.

Marcus was under a lot of pressure lately. His boss's demands were cruel and unrealistic, by anyone's standards. But with layoffs looming over everyone's shoulder, Marcus felt he had no choice but to do whatever the boss requested.

"Yes sir!" Marcus chimed into the phone. "I can have those for you first thing Monday," he promised. Dana would give anything for some of the kindness Marcus was lavishing on his boss these days. She couldn't stand to see anyone treat her dear husband so thoughtlessly and in the process steal his happiness. And to top it off, now he was stealing the kind words that used to be for her.

When Marcus hung up the phone, Dana had made a suggestion about how to handle the situation. She was only trying to help. She knew it wasn't that great of a solution, but she was just hoping to say something that would spark an idea. Usually, she was his closest ally during such conflicts.

But this time, Marcus was flustered and deep in thought. His anger toward his boss was building. He longed to use some choice words to tell him what he really thought. And it was in that moment that Dana gave her suggestion. And when she did, Marcus lashed out at her, instead. That's when he said it. And now he had to live with it.

FROM THE WORD

In military combat, the term "friendly fire" refers to casualties inflicted by

LOVE

one's fellow soldiers. In the heat of battle, it is sometimes very difficult to distinguish between allies and enemies. In a fast and furious attempt to eliminate the enemy who poses an urgent threat, comrades are accidentally destroyed instead.

The same is true in marriage. Every day, husband and wife step onto the battlefield together. When the intensity picks up, our minds often struggle to remember who the real enemy is. We can accidentally take out on our wives anger and frustrations that were originally pointed at someone else. Before you know it, you can destroy your only allied support. God provides ample protection against such mistakes throughout Proverbs.

FOR THE HEART

Soldiers carry guns, grenades, and bayonets. Husbands and wives often cripple their relationships with nothing more than their tongues.

It's no wonder James called the tongue "a fire" (James 3:6). Do you always speak to your wife with soft and tender words? If not, you might want to try this verse. Why not write it down on a piece of paper and carry it in your pocket? And when the urge to "vent" comes up, cease-fire for a moment and confirm your target. Guard your mouth and tongue. And ask God to help you respond lovingly.

You'll not only win the battle, but over time you may even win the war!

Sticks and stones can break your bones, but words can destroy your marriage!

Colossians 3:19 —

"Husbands, love your wives and do not be bitter toward them."

It was their 16th anniversary, or maybe the 17th. Mike and Colline were celebrating a tradition they had maintained since the beginning. This was the restaurant where they had their first date. It was where Mike popped the question. And it was where they had celebrated every wedding anniversary since.

Right on cue, the waiter placed a vase of six red roses on the table in front of them. Next would come the assorted appetizers, then the salads, and two filet mignons with sautéed vegetables. Afterward, they would split one slice of strawberry cheesecake.

Colline sniffed the roses and smiled. Mike made his usual comment about how the meat wasn't as tender as it used to be. The rest of the conversation would cover a wide range of topics from foreign affairs to the latest crisis at the office. Then Mike would make a toast, and they would head home.

Everything was going just as planned, until something unexpected shattered the tradition. Out of the corner of his eye, Mike noticed a young couple being escorted into the room. The hostess seated them in the small booth by the window. It was the booth Mike and Colline had called "their" booth back when they were dating. And the couple was acting just like Mike and Colline used to act in those days.

They held hands across the table. They leaned forward and whispered. And they seemed to giggle at everything the other person said. Their entire world was contained in that small booth. Everything else around them was just ornamentation.

As Mike looked on, the contrast was glaring. He and Colline had a great thing going. They got along well, they enjoyed many of the same things, and they even had a fine anniversary tradition. But as Mike observed the couple across the room, he couldn't help seeing a bit of himself in that younger man. And it was obvious that something was missing. Something had happened to the old fire.

FROM THE WORD

The original Greek language of the New Testament is very specific and exact. Where the simple word "love" appears in the English translation of Paul's letter to the Colossians, the original Greek word, "agape," is loaded with additional information. Agape love is characterized by an unceasing nature and an all-encompassing scope. The husband's love is to be expressed with genuine passion, extending to the emotional level.

And since agape love is unwavering, the husband therefore has a responsibility to maintain the emotional element of his love throughout his entire married life. Whenever he doesn't "feel" like he's in love, it's his job to restore that feeling.

FOR THE HEART

Do you still "feel" like you're in love with your wife? Or has marriage become more like a tradition? Did you know your emotions respond to the act of your will. They can be trained? When you treat your marriage with apathy, you will feel apathetic. When you decide to hold on to anger, you will feel angry. But when you choose to love, you will feel "in love" again.

If there's not a sense of emotion as you love your wife, then you're withholding. You're not giving all of yourself as agape love demands. Every husband has emotions about something. And in every case, the wife should be the primary object of her husband's emotions. Take a moment to ask God if your love for your wife contains enough emotion. And if you feel daring, why not ask your wife?

If your wife doesn't make your heart race, check your heart.

INTRODUCTION
What does it look like when you love your wife?

BIBLICAL PASSAGES ON LOVING YOUR WIFE

"Love suffers long and is kind; load does not envy; love does not parade itself, is not puffed up; does not behave rudely, does not seek its own, is not provoked, thinks no evil; does not rejoice in iniquity, but rejoices in the truth; bears all things, believes all things, hopes all things, endures all things. Love never fails." I Corinthians 13:4-8a

"Husbands, love your wives and do not be bitter toward them." Colossians 3:19

"So husbands ought to love their own wives as their own bodies; he who loves his wife loves himself. For no one ever hated his own flesh, but nourishes it and cherishes it, just as the Lord does the church." Ephesians 5:28-29

> *"There is no greater love than the love that holds on where there seems nothing left to hold onto."*
> – G. W. C. THOMAS

DISCUSSION
Why do some men believe it's impossible always to love their wives?

BIBLICAL PRINCIPLES ON LOVING YOUR WIFE (continued)

2. Love your wife as Christ "loved the church" and give yourself _____.

   A. Sacrifice means to give up something I _____ for some thing she _____.

   B. Christ loved His church enough to make the ultimate _____.

> *"This special warning concerns a foul blot in married life, when the husband as head either shows bitterness in word or deed, or in tone, to the wife or treats her with indifference, neglect, or harshness."*
> – KARL BRAUNE

3. Love your wife and do not become "_____" toward her. *Colossians 3:19*

   A. Bitter means to be sharp, cutting, _____.

   B. Never an unkind tone of voice, but always _____.

   C. Never a harsh or demeaning manner, but always _____.

   D. Never tearing down, but always _____.

   E. Never controlling, but always _____.

   "One of the great illusions of our time is that love is self-sustaining. It is not. Love must be fed and nurtured, constantly renewed."
   – DAVID R. MACE

4. Love your wife and purposefully "nourish and _____" her. *Ephesians 5:28-29*

   A. Nourish means to provide what is necessary for _____.

   B. Cherish means to treasure and treat with _____.

   "After hearing a lecture on love and marriage, one man surprised his wife with a box of candy and a dozen roses. 'Oh, this is terrible,' she said, weeping. The baby cut his finger real bad. Then I burned your dinner when I couldn't get rid of the vacuum cleaner salesman, the sink is stopped up ... and now you've come home drunk!'"
   – GARY SMALLEY

DISCUSSION
What would you tell your best friend to do if his wife said she didn't believe he loved her anymore?

CONCLUSION
Sometimes the best way to kick-start your marriage is simply to "give" your heart to your spouse. Letting go of your emotional roadblock encourages her to do the same.

L O V E

1. Name a time in everyday life when you control your emotions for the sake of the long-term good.

_____

_____

_____

2. Are you more successful controlling your emotions around strangers, or around your wife? Why?

_____

_____

_____

3. Name a situation in your marriage when loving your wife is a matter of choice and not emotion.

_____

_____

_____

4. What kind of words do you think have more power to affect a marriage: destructive words or

encouraging words? _____

_____

_____

_____

5. What are some ways you can "treasure" your wife? _____

_____

_____

_____

1 Corinthians 10:13b —

"(but God) will also make the way of escape, that you may be able to bear it."

Matt could tell he was nearing a breakthrough. At least that's what it usually meant whenever he ran out of answers. He was definitely out of answers now.

For the past several weeks, the conversation in his accountability group had centered around the subject of loving your wife. They had covered all the basic ways to make her feel loved. They talked about the best times and techniques to convey love. And each week they got together to share how they were doing.

But Matt was discovering a hole in his plan. He seemed to do fine for stretches of time. Beth even appeared to feel loved. But inevitably, Matt would experience a significant lapse every few days. And now, staring him right in the face, was the issue of continually loving.

Of all the people in his group, Matt looked to Joe for the answer. He was so steady and even-keeled. Joe listened carefully as Matt described his situation. He thought long and hard. And finally he spoke: "Matt, you use to be in the Marines, right?"

"Of course," Matt replied. Matt had not only served eight years in the Marines but had also earned many honors along the way.

Joe continued, "When your drill sergeant used to give you all those ridiculous instructions just to test your will, how did you do them all?"

Matt thought for a moment. Then the answer came to him, "One at a time, I guess."

"There's your answer," Joe smiled. Matt pondered, then realized Joe was right. He knew if he could do something once, he could do it over and over.

FROM THE WORD

One of the most tragic misconceptions is the belief that it is impossible for a normal man to succeed in obeying God. Many Christians surrender to this notion before the battle even begins. Some don't even try.

But the Bible is very clear. Sinful man is incapable of earning salvation, but as he learns to walk in the Spirit, God gives him the power to obey at all times. That's right: all times! Therefore, when God commands you to love your wife unconditionally, without stopping, He really expects you to do it — with His help.

FOR THE HEART

How about you? Do you believe it's actually possible always to love your wife, consistently nourishing and cherishing her? If you don't, then your behavior will never really move toward that goal. Don't be one of those who reasons, "Aw shucks, I'm just a humble sinner. I'm not perfect." When perfect God takes up residence in you, it should show!

God has said it. The question is not can you, but will you. Now it's time for you to respond in faith, to believe in His words and to obey His commands. Your obedience does not earn you salvation. But obedience is a natural faith response to God, acknowledging His intention to shape you in the image of Christ.

Step out in faith today, even if you only take one step.

Perfect love is perfect love.

Galatians 6:9 —

> ### "And let us not grow weary while doing good, for in due season we shall reap if we do not lose heart."

Gary and his dad, Emmett, were sitting on the old leather couch in the sunroom. This was the same leather couch where Emmett used to sit and read stories to Gary when he was a child. It was the same couch where Gary and his father had "the talk" when he was a young man. And it was the same couch where Gary's parents sat when he introduced them to the woman of his dreams.

This time, Gary and Emmett sat down as friends and two men with families. No sooner had they gotten comfortable than Gary's mother, Anne, brought in a tray with glasses of freshly squeezed lemon-aid and a plate of cookies.

"Wow, look at this!" Emmett exclaimed. "Your mother still makes the best lemon-aid." Anne smiled and disappeared out of the room again.

"Dad, what's your secret?" Gary asked.

"You kidding?" Emmett replied. "She's the one that's got me trained." Emmett laughed his trademark laugh. Gary chuckled too, then re-issued his question.

"No, seriously," Gary pried. "You and mom seem to read each other's minds sometimes. Jill and I can talk until we're blue in the face and still not understand each other. What's your secret?"

"There's no secret," Emmett went on. "When you've been married as long as we have, things just have a way of falling in place."

"Judging by some of my friends' marriages, things can also have a way of falling apart," Gary responded.

"Son," said Emmett, leaning forward in his chair, "You've been married five years. You're practically still on your honeymoon. A marriage has to grow." Emmett took a long sip from his glass, then went on, "If you keep putting good things into your marriage, eventually good things will come from it."

FROM THE WORD

You've probably heard the old saying: "true love lasts forever." It sounds nice. It has a romantic ring to it. But unfortunately, there's not much truth to it. Because it implies that if love is "true" enough, it will automatically last and last like an unstoppable force. And if it runs out, then it simply couldn't have been "true" love.

Scripture paints a different picture of love. Love is both a command and a choice, but not some unpredictable force that possesses us on its own. The love between a husband and a wife is not automatically self-sustaining; it must be renewed. What comes out of your marriage is directly related to what you put into it.

FOR THE HEART

God has revealed his design for marriage in the Bible. Each nugget of truth is a seed to be sown into your marriage. Your job is to keep planting faithfully. God provides the water and the sunlight. It may not seem like much is happening. But little by little, new sprouts begin to shoot up out of the ground. Blossoms appear. And before you know it, succulent fruit.

So how is your marriage growing? Is there a bountiful harvest of fruit in the making? Or would you say you're on the verge of famine?

Right now, jot down at least one thing that you can do today to "put good things" into your marriage. Then get busy sowing those seeds!

If you want your marriage to last, work on it first.

1 Corinthians 9:27a —

"But I discipline my body and bring it into subjection..."

Chuck drove toward home, rehearsing the conversation in his mind. He knew the right thing to do to patch things up, but this time it seemed like there was no way he was going to pull it off. As he drove, he pressed a little firmer on the accelerator and leaned a little harder into the curves of the road. He was full of all kinds of feelings and emotions, it seemed, except for love.

Brenda was anticipating the moment, too. She was dusting the furniture in the den for the second time, just to keep busy. She wanted to be there when Chuck walked in. Brenda also knew the right thing to do. But like Chuck, she went back and forth between the things she should say and the things she wanted to say.

A lot was riding on this moment. Three years ago, on Chuck's birthday, he and Brenda had an awful argument. That's when he uttered those fateful words: "I just don't love you anymore." Ever since, the two of them had been working intensely to try to put things back together.

A year of counseling with a marriage therapist seemed to go nowhere. Then, as a last ditch effort, they decided to start meeting with their pastor. It was the first time Chuck had ever heard that love, even between a man and a woman, is a choice. The pastor put it in blunt, simple terms: Chuck was commanded to love Brenda. Chuck could either obey that command or not. Suddenly, Chuck saw that his marriage problems were a simple matter of disobedience versus obedience.

Chuck flung the door open, and when their eyes met, there was a long pause. It was the moment of truth. Chuck was the first to break the silence, "Honey, I owe you a big apology."

FROM THE WORD

"Husbands love your wives." It doesn't sound very romantic. Most wives would rather hear that the husband couldn't control his love for her, not that he must be commanded to love her. But Scripture very wisely speaks to the reality of man's struggle to convey love. When it comes right down to it, love is not only a feeling or an emotion, but also a spiritual discipline.

Man is an unpredictable creature. Chances are, your whims and desires don't always support your goals of leading your family according to God's will. Therefore, Paul recognized the relevance of discipline when it comes to doing God's will. To love as God commands the husband to love, he must discipline himself often denying his inappropriate feelings and emotions. In the long run, it leads to greater feelings of love for both husband and wife.

FOR THE HEART

How do you "feel" about your wife? Have you ever felt like you don't love her anymore? Have you ever felt guilty for not having more emotional love? All marriages experience ebbs and flows. Even the best husbands sometimes don't "feel" like they're in love. That's okay! The important thing is that your actions remain consistent with those of a loving husband.

Love is a choice. Even when you feel like you don't have "anything left," you can still choose to love. If you don't, it is sin. But when you do, the feelings of love are often not far behind. *Will you resolve today to love even when you don't "feel" like it?*

When the loving gets tough, the tough get loving.

1 Corinthians 13:5 —

"Love does not seek its own..."

The package was huge. It took up all the available floor space in the living room. The bow, made of red ribbon, was the size of a basketball. Frank held both hands over Cindy's eyes as he led her into the room. "Surprise!" he exclaimed, as he quickly lifted his hands off her eyes.

Cindy smiled big. She had actually believed that Frank had forgotten her birthday. But the large, colorful box in front of her told a different story. Yep, Frank had gone all out this time. His surprise plan had been played out to perfection. But what could it be?

Cindy didn't have many things she really wanted. But as she tore open the large sheets of wrapping paper, she couldn't help imagining what was inside. It was large enough to hold the new washing machine she had seen in the catalog. Then there was the leather chair she had been eyeing for the corner of the sitting room. What surprise did her husband have in store for her? She could hardly stand the suspense.

She peeled back the final layer of wrapping paper and uncovered a bold message printed in large black letters on the side of the cardboard box: "45-inch Programmable Television With 'Picture-in-Picture.'"

Cindy forced a big smile. Frank was so excited he didn't even notice the subtle change in her expression. "Look here," he blurted, "you can watch two channels at the same time...and the remote works the VCR too."

Yep, Cindy was already familiar with those two features. She had heard them described in detail every time Frank dragged her into the electronics store. And this time, just like all the others, she wondered why in the world a person needed to watch two channels at the same time. Unless, of course, you were a big sports fan, like Frank.

FROM THE WORD

During the time that Jesus walked the earth, He often expressed His love for people by addressing their needs with a word of wisdom or a healing touch. If husbands are to love their wives the way Christ loved the church, they should examine the way He carefully met each person at the level of his or her need. To the blind, He gave sight. To the sick, He gave health.

To the insane, He gave sanity. And more than once, He gave life to the dead.

In each case, Jesus knew exactly what it took to make the other person "feel" loved. And that's precisely how husbands are commanded to love their wives also.

FOR THE HEART

Have you ever thought about what it takes to make your wife really "feel" loved? It's easy to start expressing love without ever really considering how it will be perceived. Our first instinct is to give other people what we would like to have given to us and to shower them with our own favorite things. If we like chocolate, we imagine the other person must like it too. If we like professional wrestling, then certainly other people would feel loved by receiving wrestling tickets, right? It's an honest mistake, but nonetheless, it's still a mistake.

If you really want the love you send your wife to get there, you need to give some thought to how it's packaged. What are her favorite things? Why not write down one or two things you can do today that would make your wife feel loved? If you need a few hints, go ahead and ask her.

Before you make a "love transaction," you may need a "love translation."

2 Corinthians 12:10 —

> ## "For the sake of Christ, then, I am content with... hardships..." (RSV)

Mary was drawn to the marriage retreat by its juicy title: "Opposites Attract." Curt was simply looking forward to a weekend in the mountains away from work. But as the opening exercise got under way, both were suddenly uncomfortable with what they were hearing.

For the exercise, each person answered a brief survey to determine his or her own personality type. The test included likes/dislikes, attitudes, and temperament. Then each couple compared notes to see how equally matched they were. The point of the exercise was to discover if couples were identical, or if they were in fact more like opposites.

One by one the couples stood up. And little by little, the verdict came in. Not only were they not identical, but it almost every case it seemed that they were as different as night and day. How could it be? How could so many intelligent people suffer from poor judgment on such an important subject? Is it any wonder the divorce rate is so high?

Curt and Mary both thought about their own differences. How she liked organization, and he found it confining. How he enjoyed traveling, and she preferred to stay home whenever possible. The more they thought about it, the more they realized just how different they were.

As he looked around the room at all the mismatched couples, Curt couldn't help drawing the conclusion that marriages were somehow rigged and people inevitably choose partners that bring out the worst in each other. But why?

Curt and Mary felt pretty good about how they had always worked out their differences in the past. But as they realized how many differences still remained, it was depressing. What caused this phenomenon? And what should they do about it?

FROM THE WORD

Often, the most satisfying things in life are the things that come with great difficulty like an academic degree, a business goal, an athletic pursuit, or a sales quota. The harder we work for something, the more it seems to bring fulfillment. But sometimes in marriage it's hard to see the benefit or the purpose of our difficulties. By working hard for something, we discover power and strength we otherwise would not have known. And as the apostle Paul pointed out in this passage, the ultimate discovery comes from finally tapping into God's power.

People wonder why marriage is sometimes so difficult. They have doubts, questions, and even remorse. They wonder if they married the right person after all. And they dream of reaching the point where things finally run smoother.

The hardships we question in our marriage are specifically allowed by God for a purpose. While we dream of smooth sailing, God is faithfully going about the work of molding and shaping us. The very things we disdain are actually the instruments of our refining.

FOR THE HEART

Are their certain obstacles or hardships in your marriage you think hold the key to a better life? Do you ever think, "If only we could solve that problem, kick that habit, or change that attitude, then we could have the marriage God intended us to have." Maybe it's time to embrace those hardships instead, and thank God for them.

Remember, God is still in control. As you pursue His plan for your marriage, He will faithfully transform it, in His timing. In the meantime, there may be hardships. But be encouraged. When we are weak, He is strong.

When you just can't take it any more, He still can.

LOVE

INTRODUCTION
God's design for marital love includes a built-in provision that makes it self-sustaining and continual.

BIBLICAL PRINCIPLES ON LOVING YOUR WIFE (continued)

5. Love your wife fervently and never allow your love to grow _____.

   A. Agape love includes both our actions and our _____.

   B. Agape love chooses to care deeply and lavish _____.

   C. Agape love never fails and guards against unforgiveness and _____.

> *"One loving heart sets another on fire."*
> – ST. AUGUSTINE

DISCUSSION
The next time you feel hurt, what can you do not to "tune out" or put up "the walls"?

BIBLICAL PASSAGES ON LOVING YOUR WIFE
"So God answered and said, 'You shall love the Lord your God with all your heart, with all your soul, with all your strength, and with all your mind' and 'your neighbor as yourself.'"

Luke 10:27

"And above all things have fervent love for one another, for love will cover a multitude of sins."

1 Peter 4:8

> *"Recently I asked five divorced women, individually, 'If your husband began treating you in a consistently loving manner, would you take him back?'*
>
> *"'Of course I would,' each replied. But unfortunately, none had hoped her husband would ever be like that. Because I knew one of the men personally, I had to concur with his wife's hopelessness. If he were willing to try, he could win her back. Unfortunately, he wasn't interested in learning. 'What he doesn't realize is that a lot of women are as responsive as puppy dogs,' one woman explained to me. 'If he'd come back and treat me with tenderness, gentleness and understanding, I'd take him back tomorrow.'"*
>
> – GARY SMALLEY

PERSONAL PROGRESS IN LOVING MY WIFE

PROGRESS POINTS	progress needed	progress acceptable	progress great
1. The husband unconditionally loves his wife.	☐	☐	☐
2. The husband regularly sacrifices for his wife.	☐	☐	☐
3. The husband does not become bitter or harsh.	☐	☐	☐
4. The husband nourishes and cherishes his wife.	☐	☐	☐
5. The husband fervently loves his wife and never allows his love to grow cold.	☐	☐	☐

1. I loved my wife in the early days of our relationship because she felt she was so _____

   _____

   _____

   _____.

2. The part of this session that meant the most to me about the husband loving his wife was

   _____

   _____

   _____.

3. After listening to this session, I think that I could love my wife more if I would _____

   _____

   _____

   _____.

L O V E

PRACTICAL POINTERS ON LOVING YOUR WIFE

1. _____ whatever you do that disappoints, frustrates, or angers your wife.

  A. I disappoint my wife when I _____.

  B. I frustrate my wife when I _____.

  C. I anger my wife when I _____.

2. _____ the "first works" of your early courtship. *Revelation 2:4-5*

  A. We had a great time when we _____.

  B. One special memory of early love is _____.

3. _____ your love so your wife actually feels loved.

Which would you say are the top three ways your wife feels your love? Put a 1, 2, or 3 in the top three. Then ask your wife to answer the question herself.

HUSBAND		WIFE
thinks this is what his wife would say:		*selects as her top three:*
☐	Take you out on a date?	☐
☐	Just go for a quiet walk together?	☐
☐	Plan a special weekend together?	☐
☐	Buy you a gift of flowers or clothes?	☐
☐	Enjoy sports or recreation together?	☐
☐	Share spiritual things?	☐
☐	Work on special projects with you?	☐
☐	Do something with the kids?	☐
☐	Tell you how much he loves you?	☐
☐	Sit down and really listen to you?	☐
☐	Touch you, hold your hand, kiss you?	☐
☐	Send you love notes and cards?	☐
☐	Surprise you with something special?	☐

DISCUSSION

What are you going to do to really connect with your wife and her heart?

4. _____ God's love today by believing in the Lord Jesus Christ as your personal Savior.

"For God so loved the world that He gave His only begotten Son, that whoever believes in Him should not perish but have everlasting life." John 3:16

    ☐ Today I received Jesus Christ as my personal Savior.
    ☐ Prior to today, I received Jesus Christ as my personal Savior.
    ☐ I am still considering receiving Jesus Christ as my personal Savior.

"Eve was not taken out of Adam's head to rule over him, neither out of his feet to be trampled on by him, but out of his side to be equal to him, under his arm to be protected by him, and near his heart to be loved by him."

                 – MATTHEW HENRY

PERSONAL PLEDGE

TOGETHER: We affirm today that God has called the husband to love his wife in the same way that Jesus Christ loves the church — unconditionally, sacrificially, and consistently.

HUSBAND: I commit to love you above all others and with all of my heart. I know how very important my love is to you so I pledge to loyally love you and never withdraw my love from you. I am your devoted husband and commit to nourish and cherish you as my beloved wife "til death do us part."

WIFE: I receive your love and treasure it above all others. I, too, pledge my loyalty to you and hereby commit to become the kind of wife you find easy and wonderful to love.

CONCLUSION

At any moment in time, a man can choose to love his wife. Failing to choose is equivalent to choosing not to love her.

L O V E

1. Why do you think it is so difficult to grant forgiveness?

2. When your spouse wounds you, are you more likely to get angry or withdraw and give her the "silent treatment"?

3. When in your day should you mentally "prepare" to love your wife?

4. Why does the husband's idea of loving the wife often differ from her idea?

5. Name one practical thing you can do this week to "fan the flame."

Ephesians 5: 25-33 —

> ## "Husbands, love your wives, just as Christ also loved the church and gave Himself for it."

Into the garage roared "The Man On a Mission." Home from work, and disguised as a file cabinet, Bob, Jr., spilled into the kitchen with enough briefcases, notebooks, and commotion to start a new federal agency.

Kicking the door shut, he turned around and faced them. Susan and the kids were frozen in their tracks, not sure whether to hug or hide.

"Got a HUGE presentation tomorrow at work. Bosses from headquarters are here. Got to go study this stuff and get a report ready. I'll eat later."

He failed to notice Susan's bathrobe, her pale face, puffy eyes, and haggard look. She had gone downhill rapidly all afternoon with fever and chills competing for control of her body. And the nausea! She could hardly stand up.

About 10:30 that night, Jackie appeared in the living room, now "The War Room."

"Uh, Dad, I think you better come see about Mom. She's in the bathroom moaning and groaning. I think she's about to throw up. Did you know she's been feeling sick all afternoon?

Bob stopped his work and looked up at Jackie. "She has? Okay, honey. I'll be right there."

"*She didn't look sick to me,*" Bob thought as he realized he didn't remember what she looked like when he came in earlier.

Heading upstairs, his conscience was troubled by the thoughts he was having. "*Why tonight? I don't have time to be a nurse. My entire career could be ruined if I blow this presentation tomorrow.*"

FROM THE WORD

It is not surprising that Bob's conscience was troubled. Not surprising, that is, in light of Scriptures like Ephesians 5:25.

As unrealistic as it may seem, Scripture establishes the love of Christ for the church as the example for a husband to follow in loving his wife. What does it mean to love one's wife as Christ loved the church? Sacrificially, consistently, by choice — all of that, at least. More specifically, it means when it is not convenient, when you would rather be doing something else, and especially when it might keep you from meeting your agenda!

That was Bob's situation, and he, in his heart, knew it!

FOR THE HEART

Husbands can at times resent the intrusion of their wife's needs. But husbands can learn to love as Christ loved.

Husband, is there a spot on your conscience which is a shade of gray instead of pure white? An area where your love for your wife has been less than Christ's love? You can clean that spot today by setting aside your agenda and your wants and focusing on your wife's needs. Will you do it?

When a man loves his wife sacrificially, he loves like Christ.

1 Peter 3:7-12 —

> *"Likewise you husbands, dwell with them*
> *with understanding, giving honor to the wife,*
> *as to the weaker vessel, and as being heirs together of the*
> *grace of life, that your prayers may not be hindered."*

It didn't seem to Bob, Sr., that life could look a whole lot better than it did that Saturday. The crisp, fall morning seemed to be telling Bob he was "King for a Day." He loved it. Mentally, he was already planning his agenda: First, he'd catch his two favorite Saturday morning fishing shows on television, then do his daily Bible study, then maybe spin over to a couple of sports stores and bait shops just to make sure nothing new had come in since his last visit, two days before.

"Honey, oh, h-o-n-e-y. Earth to Bob." It was Alice, gently interrupting the "King." He didn't mind. Her sweet demeanor was never an interruption. Well, rarely ever. Why did he feel an exception to the rule coming?

"I have to drive a couple of seniors from the nursing home over to the outlet mall in Blairsville, Bob. They called last night, and I just couldn't say no. I was wondering if you'd drive us over since you're free today?"

The "King" refocused out the window. His perfect Saturday kingdom had vanished! Crisp was now crummy. Fishing had become wishing. The hammock became a shopping cart, and his specialty smoked ribs, a limp mallburger. He decided to stand his ground. It's what kings do.

"Alice, I'm sorry. I have a number of things I had planned to do today. The nursing home is your ministry, and you'll just have to drive them yourself."

With that he excused himself and went to the den. His fishing shows were starting.

FROM THE WORD

The "King for a Day" crown is looking a little tarnished, wouldn't you agree? Perhaps you have experienced this in your marriage: The wife has a practical need, the importance of which the husband just does not understand. A recipe for potential conflict.

LOVE

When the Apostle Peter addressed this issue in one of his letters, he insisted that husbands live with their wives in ways that communicate and show understanding. What does understanding say to a wife? It says, "Honor." It says, "I honor you by appreciating your idea, your request, and your desire. Though it is not the same as I would do, I will honor you by helping fulfill your desire to the best of my ability." To this, Peter would probably say a hearty, "Amen!"

FOR THE HEART

When was the last time in your marriage you had an opportunity to honor your wife by showing understanding, but failed to do so?

Would you mention that "missed opportunity" to your wife today and seek her forgiveness? And, purpose to begin demonstrating understanding, by faith, if necessary! What seems like a small, insignificant gesture can crush, or blossom, the spirit of a wife.

How do you spell "honor your wife?" U-N-D-E-R-S-T-A-N-D-I-N-G.

Romans 5:6-11 —

> ### "But God demonstrates his own love toward us, in that while we were still sinners, Christ died for us."

Jack was getting in his car at Bob and Susan's when his uncle pulled in the driveway behind him.

"Uncle Bob," Jack called. "How are you doing?"

"Great, Jack. What brings you over?"

"Just dropping off some of my outgrown clothes for Bobby. Mom and Aunt Susan thought he could wear some of 'em."

"Great! Thanks for bringing them over. Hey, how's school going? Making all As, I presume. And, I've been meaning to ask you, big guy, how's the old love life? You and Sherry getting ready for the big day?"

Before Jack could answer, Bob knew he had hit a nerve. The downcast eyes, shuffling feet, and hemming and hawing were all symptoms of the this-is-worse-than-a-root-canal syndrome.

"What's wrong, Jack?" Bob asked. "Everything okay? Can I help with anything?"

"Well, you can explain women to me for starters," Jack blurted out. "I mean, I know Sherry's the right girl to marry, and all, and, yes, we're getting along fine. But man, she and I had a disagreement at school this week that I couldn't believe! That's why I'm home this weekend. I had to get away and think this through. She did something that I thought was just plain uncalled for. I didn't think people who love you would treat you that way."

"I hear you, pal. Gets rough sometimes, doesn't it?"

"Yeah. This business of love is tougher than I thought!"

FROM THE WORD

Jack, welcome to the real world! The idea that people never act inappropriately in serious relationships is a misconception. Just as moving from one country to another doesn't change your name, so moving from single to married doesn't change your nature.

Scripture shows how Christ's love for the church is a model of how husbands are to love their wives: even if they act like a sinner (see

L O V E

Romans 5:8). And while sin in marriage is a two-way street, Scripture puts upon the man the task of loving his wife with Christ-like love the same way Christ loved him, even though he is a sinner.

FOR THE HEART

Think of a time when you were the most hurt by something your wife said or did. Hurt means beyond mad. It's the "How could she have done this to me?" type of discouragement. It's the "How can we have a relationship after this?" kind of feeling. Have you truly forgiven (loved) your wife in spite of this event? Not sure? Make a list of the top three hurts you've experienced in marriage. Then forgive your wife, tear up the list, and go tell your wife how much you love her.

If you have a marriage question, love is the answer!

Psalm 128:1-3 —

> *"How happy are those who fear the Lord — all who follow his ways! You will enjoy the fruit of your labor. How happy you will be! How rich your life! Your wife will be like a fruitful vine, flourishing within your home. And look at all those children! There they sit around your table as vigorous and healthy as young olive trees." (NLT)*

"Okay, Granddad — thanks again. I'll see you Saturday."

Jack hung up the phone in his dorm room. His grandfather's grape arbor would be the perfect focus for his botany paper and the lab would begin bright and early Saturday morning.

It was early fall, harvest time, and the grapevines were bowing under the weight of the bunches. "Wow, Granddad! Look at the grapes," Jack exclaimed as they entered the arbor. "Unbelievable. How do you do it? My botany professor would be impressed!"

"Well, first you have to retire, Jack, so you can baby these things about eight to ten hours every day," laughed his grandfather. After an hour of making notes and taking pictures, Bob's voice became soft. "See this vine, Jack? It's the most fruitful one I have. I've named it 'Alice,' after you-know-who."

"Grandmother Alice?" Jack asked. "Why?"

"Because it's so fruitful. It bears so much fruit, so consistently, year after year. It just reminds me of your grandmother that way. I don't know another Christian lady who lives a more fruitful life than your Grandmother Alice.

"Jack, when your grandmother and I were first married, an old farmer I knew then who owned a vineyard, too, gave me a Bible verse to build my marriage and my home on. He said it had worked for him, and it would work for me. And it has."

"Really? Wait a minute. Let me write this down."

L O V E

FROM THE WORD

What verse would you give a young man to ensure that his wife would be like a fruitful vine in their home? If you recommended Psalm 128, you would do him a great favor.

This passage says that a man's wife will be like a fruitful vine in the very heart of their home if he will do one thing: Fear the Lord. And what is "fearing the Lord"? It is that enduring perspective of God, and one's relationship with Him, that results in awe, in worship, and in obedience to His commands. A husband who fears the Lord will have a wife who bears fruit for the Lord. But be careful! Husbands should fear the Lord because He is God, not to get a fruitful wife.

FOR THE HEART

How about you? Is it time to take a closer look at your perspective of God and your relationship with Him? How much do you fear Him? That is, how much awe, how much worship, and how much obedience to His commands can be found in your life?

Do you believe any lack of fruit in your wife's life could be tied to a lack of your fearing the Lord?

Use this moment to search your heart, and make things right with Him.

The fear of God in your life will put the fruit of God in your wife!

1 Corinthians 13:1-13 —

"And now abide faith, hope, love, these three; but the greatest of these is love."

"Larry! I thought that was you!" Dan Brennan called out, approaching Larry's booth. "Good to see you!"

Pastor Brennan's towering presence was intimidating enough. But the fact that he had married Larry and Elaine, then tried to prevent their divorce, made their encounter somewhat awkward at first.

"Hello, Pastor. How are you?" Larry managed.

"Now tell me, Larry. How is it that two classy guys like us are forced to get our nourishment from a place like The Burger Mill?" Dan Brennan was looking for an invitation to sit down.

"I don't know, just lucky I guess. Uh, would you like to sit down?" Larry said.

"Sure. Thanks. Don't mind if I do. I'm here by myself between meetings. So, how are you?"

"Oh, I'm doing okay, I guess. Still trying to figure out what went wrong with Elaine and me. I've never had a chance to thank you for all you did to try to help us, Pastor. It meant a lot. Maybe we just weren't ready to hear what we needed to hear. Do you think that's possible?"

"Sure, it's possible. You and Elaine went through some deep water together. All of us probably have to learn some things the hard way. I know I have! You know, Larry, as I've reflected on your divorce from Elaine, and all of the things we talked about in counseling, it seems there was one key ingredient missing in your marriage."

"Are you kidding? There had to be more than one thing missing!"

FROM THE WORD

Scripture is very clear about what has the highest value in God's kingdom. Without question, it is love. God Himself is called "love," and Jesus commanded us to love God and our neighbor above all else. Surely this ethical priority holds true in marriage, the most important and intense of all human relationships. The Apostle Paul seemed to think so as he instructed the believers at Corinth. To paraphrase 1 Corinthians 13:13

L O V E

in the language of husbands: "A husband can be spiritual, he can be optimistic, he can be loyal and kind. He can be lots of wonderful things. But above all, the greatest thing he can be toward his wife is loving." Without love, his actions are like sounding brass.

FOR THE HEART

Husband, as we end this series of devotionals designed to encourage you to love your wife, take a quick inventory. Jot down the top five positive things you think you "are" to your wife, for example: provider, friend, or encourager. Does "lover" (and not just in the physical sense) rank #1? Is the greatest thing on your list "love"?

If not, can you make a commitment before God today to begin to love your wife in new and meaningful ways?

Loving husbands are easy to find. Just look for happy wives.

During courtship and early marriage, expressing love is relatively easy. As time goes by, however, demonstrating true love may become a bit more challenging. It is not uncommon to hear from someone considering divorce, "But we just don't love each other anymore."

That may even be true in your marriage, but the situation is not hopeless. Christ-like love can be nurtured in your marriage. Discover the joy of obedience as you allow God's word to impact you...and your marriage.

1. *Love's commitment Ephesians 5:25-29*

How is the husband to love his wife?

What does it mean for a husband to "nourish" and "cherish" his wife?

In your marriage, how does the wife respond when she is nourished and cherished by her husband?

In what two ways could the husband nourish and cherish the wife that would make the greatest difference in your marriage?

2. *Love's contrast Proverbs 15:17*

What attitude can bring great unhappiness to a home even when there is an abundance of possessions?

What are some of the ways that hatred can manifest itself in a marriage?

Identify a time in your marriage when an unloving attitude brought great unhappiness.

In your marriage, what does the husband do or say that makes the wife feel unloved the most?

What have you observed to be the consequences of unkind comments or actions by the husband toward the wife?

3. *Love's choice Genesis 24-67*

What is stated in this verse about Isaac's relationship to Rebekah?

What emotions does a wife feel when she knows her husband has chosen to love her?

_____

What are some of the things the wife does in your marriage that make it difficult for the husband to express love to her?

_____

In your marriage, what is the most important thing the husband could choose to do to cause the wife to feel loved?

_____

_____

4. *Love's praise* Proverbs 31:28-29

In this passage, how does the husband express his love?

_____

What impact can genuine praise have on a wife?

_____

List three characteristics of your spouse that are praiseworthy.

_____

Describe how you will express praise to your spouse today.

_____

5. *Love's sacrifice* Genesis 29:18-20

How did Jacob demonstrate the depth of his love for Rachel?

_____

In your marriage, describe a time when the husband demonstrated sacrificial love for the wife.

_____

How does the wife wish the husband would be more sacrificial right now in your marriage?

_____

Husband, will you commit (or recommit) yourself to love your wife as God has commanded?
Demonstrate your commitment by initialing and dating this page.

_____   _____
YOUR INITIALS   TODAY'S DATE

Transformers:

With Scripture on one side and a prayer on the other, these cards will help provide the daily discipline you need to stay committed to your wife and marriage. Each of the six video sessions comes with two cards, one for morning and one for the afternoon/evening. Use the same two session cards every day for a week, and be sure to check off the days of the week in the boxes provided. Before long, you'll feel those verses sinking deep into your soul. And transforming all that you are.

SESSION 1 — The Morning Transformer

TRANSFORMATION THRU RENEWING THE MIND

Ephesians 5:23-24

23 For the husband is head of the wife, as also Christ is head of the church; and He is the Savior of the body.

24 Therefore, just as the church is subject to Christ, so let the wives be to their own husbands in everything.

Su	M	Tu	W	Th	F	Sa

SESSION 1 — The Evening Transformer

TRANSFORMATION THRU RENEWING THE MIND

1 Corinthian 11:3

3 But I want you to know that the head of every man is Christ, the head of woman is man, and the head of Christ is God.

1 Corinthians 11:8-9

8 For man is not from woman, but woman from man.

9 Nor was man created for the woman, but woman for the man.

Su	M	Tu	W	Th	F	Sa

SESSION 2 — The Morning Transformer

TRANSFORMATION THRU RENEWING THE MIND

Mark 10:42-43

42 But Jesus called them to Himself and said to them, "You know that those who are considered rulers over the Gentiles lord it over them, and their great ones exercise authority over them.

43 "Yet it shall not be so among you; but whoever desires to become great among you shall be your servant."

Luke 10:34-35

34 So he went to him and bandaged his wounds, pouring on oil and wine; and he set him on his own animal, brought him to an inn, and took care of him.

35 On the next day, when he departed, he took out two denarii; gave them to the innkeeper, and said to him, "Take care of him; and whatever more you spend, when I come again, I will repay you."

Su	M	Tu	W	Th	F	Sa

TRANSFORMATION THRU PRAYER OF THE HEART

Dear Master,

Thank You for this new day! You have watched and guarded me through the night like a faithful Servant. Your Glory radiates in the heavens, and yet You have chosen to serve me with Your merciful love!

Lord, Your loving example demonstrates for me how I am to love my wife. Your lovingkindness refreshes me and fuels me for the task. How I praise You for working in my heart and for strengthening me as I seek to be the faithful Head of my family.

Omniscient God, there may be unforeseen events in the day ahead. There may be potential stresses and distractions that seek to draw me away from effective leadership. Thank You that in Your eyes, nothing is unforeseen! Thank You for going before me today. Thank You for "hemming me in" and securing my way. With You as my Head, I can in turn be the Head of my wife. Amen.

TRANSFORMATION THRU PRAYER OF THE HEART

Dear Heavenly Father,

How wonderful You are! No one is as compassionate or merciful or loving as You! You are my Heavenly Father and always shower your loyal love upon me. You never stop seeking my best! You know everything about me and yet You—Almighty God—still love me! Oh, Lord, how wonderful You are!

Because of all Your mercies, I come directly into your Presence through the Blood of Jesus and bow before Your Throne. You've not asked something from me, You've asked something for me. You request that I voluntarily give myself wholeheartedly to You as a living sacrifice. You have ordained that I should be the Head of my wife—what a thought! Lord, when I consider what kind of person I am—and what kind of Person You are—my heart yearns to obey You and lead as You have commanded. So, I present myself to You—You are my Lord. And by Your Power, I will be my wife's Head. Amen!

TRANSFORMATION THRU PRAYER OF THE HEART

Dear Heavenly Father,

I come before You this morning in recognition that You are the Head of all things. You have ordained all creation and determined the order of all things. You alone, oh God, are worthy of lifting man up and putting him down!

I humbly confess to You my sin because I have not fully accepted Your will for my life in the area of headship. I bow in humble acknowledgement that You have ordained me to be the head of my wife, and the leader of my family.

I submit to You and to this special calling on my life. I commit to answer Your call by diligently seeking to learn Your design for the Head and to faithfully perform the duties You have set before me. Help me, my Head and my Guide, to learn Your will and apply myself in a manner that pleases You. Please help me today to recognize ways in which I can serve as Head. In the name of Jesus, Amen.

...Did you know that you can enjoy the life-changing message of *Leading & Loving* wherever you go? Take the teaching into your car, your kitchen, or even the office. The **Audio Album** features six audiocassettes with each 26-minute session from the video series — along with one free workbook. To order, call (800) 763-5433, and request item number 66300 for $19.95.

SESSION 2 — *The Evening Transformer*

TRANSFORMATION THRU RENEWING THE MIND

1 Timothy 3:2, 4-5

2 A bishop then must be blameless, the husband of one wife, temperate, sober-minded, of good behavior, hospitable, able to teach;

4 one who rules his own house well, having his children in submission with all reverence

5 (for if a man does not know how to rule his own house, how will he take care of the church of God?);

1 Timothy 5:8

8 But if anyone does not provide for his own, and especially for those of his household, he has denied the faith and is worse than an unbeliever.

Su	M	Tu	W	Th	F	Sa

SESSION 3 — *The Morning Transformer*

TRANSFORMATION THRU RENEWING THE MIND

John 10:13-15

13 The hireling flees because he is a hireling and does not care about the sheep.

14 I am the good shepherd; and I know My sheep, and am known by My own.

15 As the Father knows Me, even so I know the Father; and I lay down My life for the sheep.

1 Peter 3:7

7 Husbands, likewise, dwell with them with understanding, giving honor to the wife, as to the weaker vessel, and as being heirs together of the grace of life, that your prayers may not be hindered.

Su	M	Tu	W	Th	F	Sa

SESSION 3 — *The Evening Transformer*

TRANSFORMATION THRU RENEWING THE MIND

Ephesians 5:25-27

25 Husbands, love your wives, just as Christ also loved the church and gave Himself for her,

26 that He might sanctify and cleanse her with the washing of water by the word,

27 that He might present her to Himself a glorious church, not having spot or wrinkle or any such thing, but that she should be holy and without blemish.

Su	M	Tu	W	Th	F	Sa

TRANSFORMATION THRU PRAYER OF THE HEART

Dear Heavenly Father,

You are the perfect, righteous, and faithful Ruler of the universe! You lead with justice and purity! But I, oh merciful God, am imperfect.

At times I am weak and inadequate to carry out Your command to be the Head of my wife and my family. Cleanse me, Holy Father, and set me on a right path this very moment. Turn my heart, right now, to servant-hood. Cause my heart to see its purpose as You have commanded it, and cause my whole being to yearn to be a faithful servant. Lord, as this day wears on and as night approaches, make me keenly sensitive and alert to my wife's needs. Help me to provide for her needs and, thus, to rule my own house. Help me to lead with tenderness and meekness. Lord, I confess that this responsibility is too much for me to handle alone. My other duties sometimes weigh heavily on me. Thank You that You have promised to walk with me every step of the way, and that You ensure my success while I walk with you. In Jesus' name, Amen.

TRANSFORMATION THRU PRAYER OF THE HEART

Good Morning Lord!

Thank You, Lord, that I don't awaken to face today alone! Thank You that even before I opened my eyes, You were right here ready to guide me to fulfill your Holy calling on my life. Thank You that You are here even now, as I face this new day and take up my charge to be the Head of this family.

Father, You are full of tenderness and mercy. But, I confess, I am not always so. I need You to live through me today. I need Your Strength to help me take up my mantle as the Head of my wife. Only by Your Power can I faithfully carry out this duty.

Lord, help me today to grasp the concept of being a strong leader, and yet dwelling with understanding. Show me, today, how to give honor to my wife as the weaker vessel. Put in me, oh Lord, a servant's spirit. Help me to lay down my life for my wife. Lead me, step-by-step, in the way.

TRANSFORMATION THRU PRAYER OF THE HEART

Lord of the day and night,

I come to You in the middle of another day—another incredible day that You have created! In my Spirit, I step out of the daily grind and into the beauty of your awesome Holiness! I long for You to refresh me with Your perspective on this day. Help me to see Your vantage point, and the paths that you have laid for me.

Lord, You have given me Jesus—the Head of the church—as my role model. Just as He sanctifies me and cleanses me, help me to lead my wife toward holiness and purity. Just as He prepares me to be presented to Himself, show me how to bring my wife to her full glory.

Father, I see that my own humility and servant leadership form the foundation for this important task. Once again, I must turn to You—the Source of my Strength—for my Power. Equip me and empower me to finish this day strong! Thank You for victory! In Jesus' name, Amen!

TRANSFORMATION THRU RENEWING THE MIND

Ephesians 5:28-29

28 So husbands ought to love their own wives as their own bodies; he who loves his wife loves himself.

29 For no one ever hated his own flesh, but nourishes and cherishes it, just as the Lord does the church.

Ephesians 5:33

33 Nevertheless let each one of you in particular so love his own wife as himself, and let the wife see that she respects her husband.

Su	M	Tu	W	Th	F	Sa

TRANSFORMATION THRU RENEWING THE MIND

Colossians 3:19

19 Husbands, love your wives and do not be bitter toward them."

1 Corinthians 13:4-8a

4 Love suffers long and is kind; love does not envy; love does not parade itself, is not puffed up;

5 does not behave rudely, does not seek its own, is not provoked, thinks no evil;

6 does not rejoice in iniquity, but rejoices in the truth;

7 bears all things, believes all things, hopes all things, endures all things.

8 Love never fails.

Su	M	Tu	W	Th	F	Sa

TRANSFORMATION THRU RENEWING THE MIND

Matthew 5:44-46

44 But I say to you, love your enemies, bless those who curse you, do good to those who hate you, and pray for those who spitefully use you and persecute you,

45 that you may be sons of your Father in heaven; for He makes His sun rise on the evil and on the good, and sends rain on the just and on the unjust.

46 For if you love those who love you, what reward have you? Do not even the tax collectors do the same?

I John 3:16

16 By this we know love, because He laid down His life for us. And we also ought to lay down our lives for the brethren.

Su	M	Tu	W	Th	F	Sa

TRANSFORMATION THRU PRAYER OF THE HEART

Everlasting Father,

Another day dawns, reminding me of Your faithfulness. Your consistent, everlasting love amazes me! Thank You that Your love never fails.

I confess that I am not worthy of Your love. I have used You, ignored You, and tried to manipulate You. But You love me still! Your love is unconditional. Your love is sacrificial. Although I sometimes run away, Your love pursues me!

Teach me Your ways, oh Lord! Lead me in Your Truth and teach me. Put in my heart a love like Yours. Help me now to love my wife the way You love me. When I feel like she doesn't deserve my love, help me to love as You have commanded. When she rejects my love, help me to love in a way that pursues her even more. By Your power I pray these things. Amen!

TRANSFORMATION THRU PRAYER OF THE HEART

Author of Love,

I come to You now for refreshment! Lord, I tire from the activities of the day, but You never tire. My Love often grows weary, but Your Love endures forever. Stir my heart with Your love, Lord! Fill my heart until it overflows to those around me.

I confess, righteous Father, that I have often loved only in part. Many times I have behaved rudely, sought my own, thought evil, and been easily provoked. Your Love, oh Lord, abides forever! Cleanse me now from my impurities, and fill me with Your tireless love.

You have commanded me to love my wife as Christ loved the church. Just as He was faithful to the finish, help me, Father, to finish this day strong. In Jesus' name, Amen.

TRANSFORMATION THRU PRAYER OF THE HEART

Heavenly Father,

You are the Author of love, and Your love abounds beyond what I could ever imagine! Even while I was sleeping, You have been loving me... constantly and faithfully. And now as I awake, You love me still. As I walk through the day, Your love for me will never diminish, pause, or dwindle!

Father, I confess ignoring Your love. I become preoccupied with seeking after other things. I repent now, and turn my face toward You, embracing the full measure of Your love for me. By Your Power, help me to reflect Your love to everyone I will see today. Most of all, guide me to show love for my wife as I would for my own flesh. It is in Your name that I pray. Amen.

TRANSFORMATION THRU RENEWING THE MIND

John 13:34-35

34 A new commandment I give to you, that you love one another; as I have loved you, that you also love one another.

35 By this all will know that you are My disciples, if you have love for one another.

Su	M	Tu	W	Th	F	Sa

TRANSFORMATION THRU RENEWING THE MIND

Luke 10:27

27 So he answered and said, "You shall love the Lord your God with all your heart, with all your soul, with all your strength, and with all your mind," and "your neighbor as yourself."

1 Peter 4:8-9

8 And above all things have fervent love for one another, for "love will cover a multitude of sins."

9 Be hospitable to one another without grumbling.

Su	M	Tu	W	Th	F	Sa

TRANSFORMATION THRU RENEWING THE MIND

I John 4:19-21

19 We love Him because He first loved us.

20 If someone says, "I love God," and hates his brother, he is a liar; for he who does not love his brother whom he has seen, how can he love God whom he has not seen?

21 And this commandment we have from Him: that he who loves God must love his brother also.

Su	M	Tu	W	Th	F	Sa

TRANSFORMATION THRU PRAYER OF THE HEART

Lord of Love, I have sought success all my life.
At times I have made great accomplishments.
At times I have achieved major goals. I have called this success. But thank You, merciful God, that You have revealed to me Your definition of success: to love.

Father, I embrace this new commandment. I commit myself to love as I have been loved by You. I honor You with the first fruits of my love. And I acknowledge that by your design, I am to love my wife even as I would my own body. As I accomplish this new goal, by Your Power, may Your name be glorified as we fulfill your command to love each other. Amen.

TRANSFORMATION THRU PRAYER OF THE HEART

Dear Heavenly Father,
You know me better than I know myself. While I have sought pleasure and convenience, You have pursued my holiness and purity. Thank You for always looking out for my best interests! I submit myself to Your purposes for my life.

Just as You have put my needs first in this way, help me also to put the needs of my wife first. Transform my love to make it selfless and pure. Help me as I seek to know her needs as well as she knows them herself. In the loving name of Jesus, Amen!

TRANSFORMATION THRU PRAYER OF THE HEART

Dear Lord,
Sometimes it is hard to love as You have commanded me to love. I have said, "I love God," but I have not always shown love for my wife. Although Your love never ceases, my love often fails.

I acknowledge that You desire for me to love my wife without ceasing. I believe that it is actually possible for me to obey You completely in this area. I profess that I can do all things through Christ who strengthens me. Strengthen me, Lord, for this task. In Jesus' name I pray, Amen.